OCR
Medicine
Investigations

COLIN SHEPHARD   ROSEMARY REES

SINGULAR EFFECTS OF THE UNIVERSAL _VEGETABLE_ PILLS ON A GREEN GROCER! _A FACT!_

Who _Green'un_ like was order'd to live for the space of one Month upon _Vegetable_ Diet & to Take during that time 132 Boxes of _Vegetable_ Pills for the Cure of a Gan_green_. & being caught in a Shower of Rain in the _Green_ Fields in the evening of the 1ˢᵗ of April last. was put to Bed midst _Shooting_ pains. & in the Morning presented the above Phenomenon of a Moving Kitchen Garden !!!

Query ___ Is he not one of the _Productive Classes_

JOHN MURRAY

Mark schemes

Mark schemes for the source investigations in Part 2 can be downloaded free of charge from www.hoddersamplepages.co.uk. Alternatively, you can call 020 7873 6000 and ask for the Educational Marketing department.

The medicine game

A copy of the game on pages 90–91 is available in colour to download from the website as above.

This book is for our parents: Joyce and Eddie; Con and Ellis.

© Colin Shephard and Rosemary Rees 2004

First published in 2004
by John Murray (Publishers) Ltd, a member of the Hodder Headline Group
338 Euston Road
London NW1 3BH
Reprinted 2004

Layouts by Christina Newman, Black Dog Design
Illustrations by Phil Garner/Beehive Illustration, Mike Humphries/Clifton Graphics
Typeset in 11/12 pt Bodoni Book by Servis Filmsetting Ltd, Manchester
Printed and bound in Dubai by Oriental Press

A catalogue entry for this title is available from the British Library

ISBN 0 7195 7745 4

Contents

ACKNOWLEDGEMENTS

Photo credits

The Publishers would like to thank the following for permission to reproduce copyright material:

Cover & frontispiece Wellcome Library, London; **p.1** Werner Forman Archive/Private Collection, Holland; **p.3** Private Collection/Bridgeman Art Library; **p.4** The Trustees of the Weston Park Foundation/Bridgeman Art Library; **p.5** Punch Library & Archive; **p.6** Mary Evans Picture Library; **p.7** American Museum of Natural History Library (Image No. 333696); **p.10** The Trustees of the Weston Park Foundation/Bridgeman Art Library; **p.12** Punch Library & Archive; **p.18** The Art Archive/National Archaeological Museum, Athens/Dagli Orti; **p.24** By permission of the British Library (Add. Ms 17987 f.101); **p.25** *tl* By permission of the Syndics of Cambridge University Library (Ms Ee.3.59 f.21v), *tr* By permission of the British Library (Harl. 3140, f.39), *b* By permission of the British Library (Sloane 1977, f.50v); **p.26** Bibliothèque Nationale, Paris/Bridgeman Art Library; **p.27** Hulton Archive; **p.28** Hulton Archive; **p.30** Musée de l'Hôtel Sandelin, Saint-Omer, France/Bridgeman Art Library; **p.31** *l* Wellcome Library, London; **p.32** The Royal Collection © 2003, Her Majesty Queen Elizabeth II (photo: Eva Zielinska-Millar); **p.35** Wellcome Library, London; **p.36** *t & b* Wellcome Library, London; **p.40** *t* Private Collection/Bridgeman Art Library, *b* The Art Archive/Private Collection/Eileen Tweedy; **p.42** The Trustees of the Weston Park Foundation/Bridgeman Art Library; **p.43** Mary Evans Picture Library; **p.46** Mary Evans Picture Library; **p.47** Wellcome Library, London; **p.48** Mary Evans Picture Library; **p.50** *t* British Museum, London/Bridgeman Art Library, *b* Wellcome Library, London; **p.51** *t & b* Guildhall Library, Corporation of London; **p.52** Punch Library & Archive; **p.55** *t* Wellcome Library, London, *b* Mary Evans Picture Library; **p.57** Wellcome Library, London; **p.59** Hulton Archive; **p.60** © Copyright The British Museum; **p.61** *t & b* Punch Library & Archive; **p.62** © Hutchison Library/Bernard Regent; **p.63** *l & r* courtesy WHO; **p.64** Alexander Fleming Laboratory Museum, St Mary's Hospital, London; **p.65** Alexander Fleming Laboratory Museum, St Mary's Hospital, London; **p.68** Atlantic Syndication (photo: Centre for the Study of Cartoons and Caricature, University of Kent); **p.69** *t* © Express Newspapers, *b* Punch Library & Archive; **p.72** *t* Wellcome Library, London, *b* Punch Library & Archive; **p.74** The Pierpont Morgan Library, New York © 2003 (photo: Pierpont Morgan Library/Art Resource/Scala, Florence); **p.75** *t* Private Collection/Bridgeman Art Library, *b* U.S. National Library of Medicine, Bethesda, Maryland; **p.76** *t* Wellcome Library, London, *c* Hulton Archive, *b* Courtesy of the Royal College of Nursing Archives, from '*Fifty Years*', supplement to *Nursing Record*, 20 December 1888; **p.77** *l* Wellcome Library, London, *r* Science Museum/Science and Society Picture Library.

t = top, *b* = bottom, *l* = left, *r* = right, *c* = centre

Every effort has been made to trace all copyright holders, but if any has been inadvertently overlooked the Publishers will be pleased to make the necessary arrangements at the first opportunity.

Written sources

p.33 *H & I* Colin Shephard; **p.39** *D* from *Doctor Jenner of Berkeley* by Dorothy Fisk, *E* Colin Shephard, *F* from *Edward Jenner* by Richard Fisher; **p.55** *E* Colin Shephard; **p.62** *I* from *Homeopathy A–Z* by Dana Ullman; **p.64** *B* from *The Life of Sir Alexander Fleming* by Andre Maurois; **p.65** *C* from *Alexander Fleming* by Gwyn MacFarlane; *D* Colin Shephard; **p.70** *J* from *The People's War* by Angus Calder.

Part 1

Introduction

How to use historical sources

During your study of the history of medicine you are going to be using lots of historical sources to find out about the past. You will also have to answer questions about sources in the examination. The first section of this book has been written to give you some help with answering these questions.

Why it's important to know something!

Some people think that source questions are easy because you do not need to know anything – you can work out the answer from the sources. How wrong they are. It's true that you need to study the sources carefully but to make sense of them you need to know quite a lot about the topic as well. Study the source below. See if you can work out what is happening in the picture and what the message of the artist was. Make a list of as many points as you can.

● **SOURCE 1**

How many of the following points did you get?

- It shows a Japanese woman who has married a western man.
- The baby (shown with his nursemaid) is the product of their marriage.
- The baby is shown as violent and has a beard and lots of hair because the Japanese thought of all westerners as 'hairy barbarians'.

And what was the purpose of the picture?

The drawing is obviously anti-western. It is a warning to Japanese girls not to marry the horrible barbarians (westerners) by showing what will happen if they do – they will have a child who is hairy and aggressive! Of course, the artist does not really think that babies like this one would be born. He is using this threat to get across the idea that westerners are horrible and so the Japanese should have nothing to do with them.

How do we know all this?

The picture was drawn in the 1860s when westerners were beginning to make contact with Japan. Commodore Perry, an American, had made the first contact in 1853. He was followed by other westerners who wanted to trade with Japan. Some of the Japanese did not want anything to do with the westerners. They thought the westerners were uncivilised barbarians and wanted them to go away. The picture was clearly drawn by someone of these views.

You probably did not work all this out! After all, you are not studying the history of Japan. But you can probably now see that to understand what the picture is about you need to know something about the background. Study the drawing on the page opposite. Its subject is something you should know about. With a partner, discuss what is happening in the drawing and what its message is. Then look at the points below and see how many you came up with.

- You probably recognise this picture. You probably know straight away that it is about Jenner's vaccination for smallpox.
- You probably know that this drawing was published in 1802, which was not long after Jenner's discovery of his vaccine in 1796.
- You probably know that, at first, there was a lot of opposition to Jenner's vaccine. Many people did not like the idea of injecting matter from an animal into a human being. They were worried about the after-effects.
- You have probably worked out that this drawing clearly refers to these worries. You are able to make sense of it by using your knowledge of Jenner and his vaccine.

What did you think was the message of the drawing? See if you came up with one of the suggestions given below the drawing on the page opposite.

● SOURCE 2

Jenner's assistant giving a dose of 'OPENING MIXTURE' to a patient who has not yet been vaccinated. The mixture has been made partly from vomit (the bottle can be seen on the table). The artist is implying that this mixture is given to people before they are vaccinated.

Jenner vaccinating a terrified looking woman.

People who have been vaccinated. They have parts of cows growing out of their bodies: a pregnant woman is delivering a cow from beneath her skirt, a man is sprouting cowhorns!

A boy holding a tub labelled 'VACCINE POCK hot from ye COW'.

A cartoon called 'The Cow-Pock – or – The Wonderful Effects of the new Inoculation. The publication of the Anti-Vaccine Society'. (1802).

What is the message of the drawing?

This is a much harder question. You could say that the drawing is criticising the vaccine by saying that it is dangerous to people. The artist is not really saying that cows would start growing out of people – he has drawn this to get across the idea that vaccination is dangerous.

Or ...

You could say that what is happening in the picture is so silly that no one would believe it. Perhaps the artist is showing how silly the criticisms of Jenner are. The artist could be supporting Jenner and his vaccine.

These are two different interpretations of the drawing. An examiner would accept either because they both make sense. The important thing is that you explain your interpretation by referring to details in the drawing and to your knowledge of the topic.

Making sense of unusual sources

Because the history of medicine covers strange topics, some of the sources are going to be rather unusual. This makes them all the more interesting. See if you can make sense of the two sources that follow.

● **SOURCE 3**

In the background are doctors who are ignoring what is going on. This is to show how dissections are beneath them and are carried out by inferiors like surgeons.

Surgeons invited pupils and friends to watch. Look at their faces. What are their reactions to the dissection?

The artist has a pulley and rope pulling the head up to make the corpse look alive. This is connected with people's fears of surgeons dissecting people who were still alive.

Are the surgeon and his assistants made to look cruel and callous or careful and sensitive by the type of knife held by the surgeon and by the fact that one of his assistants is gouging out the eye of the corpse?

Why has the artist drawn a noose around the corpse's neck?

Why has the artist drawn a dog eating the corpse's heart?

An engraving called 'The Reward of Cruelty', 1751.

This drawing shows the body of Tom Nero being dissected. In the eighteenth century a certain number of bodies of executed criminals were handed over to the Company of Surgeons every year for dissection, for the benefit of their students. Nero had begun his life of crime by being cruel to animals (this is the cruelty in the title of the picture). He later murdered his mistress and was hanged. His body was handed over to the Company of Surgeons for dissection. This was regarded as a fate worse than death. Christians believed that their bodies would be resurrected at the Day of Judgement. This could not happen if your body had been dissected.

The fact that surgeons carried out dissections made people scared of them and added to the view that they were cruel and not bothered about the suffering of their patients. There was also a fear that if the hangman did not do his job properly prisoners might be dissected while they were still alive. This happened in 1740 to William Duell who suddenly sat up during his dissection. Thankfully, the surgeons had not got very far. Duell was given some wine and was later reprieved from the death penalty.

Use the drawing and all the information above to see if you can answer this question, 'What message did the artist want to give about surgeons?'

Cartoons

The drawings we have been looking at so far are cartoons. You can see that the artists deliberately did not draw realistic pictures. What they drew was often fantastic, exaggerated, even mad. They did this to get a message across.

● **SOURCE 4**

A cartoon about the River Thames called 'The Silent Highwayman. Your money or your life', published in 1858.

Is this cartoon realistic – do skeletons row boats? Of course they don't. Does this mean the cartoon has no use to us as historians? Of course it doesn't. What we have to do is work out what point the artist was making.

Look at the cartoon carefully. In pairs, discuss these questions and write down some brief answers. Then write an answer to the question, 'Why do you think this cartoon was published in 1858?'

- What is the skeleton meant to represent? (What do skeletons usually represent?)
- Why has the artist drawn dead animals in the river?
- What is the overall impression you get from the picture – is it happy, wonderful, gloomy, threatening – or something else?
- Why is it called 'The Silent Highwayman'?
- Why does it say 'Your money or your life'?
- Does the date matter? What was going on around this time that has something to do with this cartoon? Was there anything going on in 1858 in particular?

Photographs

Some students think that photographs must show the truth because they show something that was really there. This seems to make sense, but is sometimes wrong.

Sometimes photographs can be set up. A photographer might ask people to do something and then take a photograph of them. Sometimes a photograph can even be faked, although this is rare. In all cases the photographer will have made a deliberate decision to take a particular photograph, and as historians we need to ask why he or she did that.

The photograph that follows is a good example of how photographs can be useful, but can also give us problems. It shows some of the dreadful conditions that the Liberal government tried to put right at the beginning of the twentieth century. The Liberals had to convince people that reforms were needed. The photograph is genuine; it shows the real conditions in which this family lived. But think a minute – how and why was the photograph taken? The photographer must have deliberately gone into this house to take this particular shot. Why?

● **SOURCE 5**

The photographer probably wanted to show everyone the dreadful conditions some people were living in. This does not make the photograph untrustworthy, but it does mean we should use it carefully. The photographer might have chosen the worst conditions he could find. This photograph does not mean there were lots of people living like this. We would have to use knowledge of that time to make a judgement.

- Has the photographer changed the way this family behave?
- Do you think they usually sit like that?
- Has one of the boys been asked to go to bed (maybe suggesting he is ill)?
- Has the mother been asked to lean over the boy in a concerned way?

So be careful with photographs. They can be very useful, but they have to be used with caution.

Objects and artefacts

The cartoons we have been looking at were deliberately created by the artist to tell people something about medicine. Other sources that we use to study the history of medicine have been left from the past just by accident. They are things that simply existed at the time, for example the skulls of people who lived in the past, or objects they made in their everyday lives. They were not made deliberately to tell us things, but we can still learn a lot from them.

● **SOURCE 6**

Look at the picture on the left. The object it shows comes from the Tlingit people who live on the south-east coast of Alaska. Discuss with the person sitting next to you what you think it is. It does have something to do with medicine! Look at it carefully. Look for clues and remember what you have learned about the beliefs of other civilisations like the Aborigines.

You probably worked out that the object is a mask.

- What kind of person would be most likely to wear it?
- Why would they wear it?
- Why does it have bird skin, blue jay (a type of bird) feathers and bearskin attached to it?
- Would the person wearing it believe in natural or supernatural causes of disease?

Have you come up with an answer similar to this?

The people who used this mask had supernatural beliefs about illness. They believed that bad spirits could interfere with people's lives. One thing the spirits could do was to make people ill. Only the medicine man (or shaman) could break the power of these evil spirits. To do this he needed the help of good spirits. When he was wearing the mask he could see the spirit world and call on the help of the spirits of animals. They would help draw out the bad spirit from the person who was ill.

You probably got quite close to this explanation by looking at the mask carefully and by using your knowledge of people's beliefs in spirits.

Written sources

You might think, by now, that written sources are easier to use than drawings or objects. With the latter there is quite a lot of working out to do, but surely written sources simply mean what they say? Unfortunately, this is often not the case and we also have to do a lot of work to make sense of written sources.

Read the source that follows. It is a letter from Lord Londonderry to a London newspaper in 1831, at the start of an outbreak of cholera in Britain.

● SOURCE 7

I intend to put the public's mind at rest about cholera in Sunderland. I live within five miles of the town and have taken great trouble to be informed about the subject. I feel quite satisfied that reports of this fatal disease have been greatly exaggerated. I am so convinced that I shall not remove either my family or myself from the area.

I enclose with this letter a letter from Dr Brown, an old army medical officer who served with me, and who is now in constant attendance on my family.

What are your first impressions of Lord Londonderry and his letter?

Here are a few facts about Lord Londonderry. They will make you look at the letter in a different way. Londonderry was the richest and most powerful coal owner in the north-east of England. He wanted to sell his coal and he did this by sending it by ship from Sunderland. However, the government had stopped all ships entering and leaving Sunderland in an attempt to stop the cholera from spreading.

Are you becoming a bit suspicious about Londonderry's letter?
And here is another thing: the letter from Dr Brown, which Londonderry mentions, claimed that people only suffered from cholera because they were weak through drinking too much alcohol and that the banning of ships from entering and leaving Sunderland was not necessary because the disease was not infectious.

Now answer these questions:

- What do you think Londonderry is up to?
- Do you trust what he says in his letter?

You probably decided that you do not trust Londonderry. Does this make his letter useless to historians like us? No, it doesn't. Many students make the mistake in exams of saying that biased sources are no use. **Never write this**. Write down what we can learn from Londonderry's letter.

Luckily, not all written sources are as tricky as Londonderry's letter. Read this poem from ancient Egypt:

● SOURCE 8

It is seven days from yesterday since I saw my love,
And sickness has crept over me,
My limbs have become heavy,
I cannot feel my own body.
If the master-doctors come to me
I gain no comfort from their remedies.
And the priest-magicians have no cures,
My sickness is not diagnosed.
My love is better by far for me than any remedies.
She is more important than all the books of medicine.

You can learn lots from this source about Egyptian medicine and not just the obvious things like the author was feeling ill and he was in love. Write down the answers to these questions and see what you have learned. Explain each answer using the evidence in the source.

- Why did the author turn to priest-magicians?
- Did the Egyptians believe in natural or supernatural methods, or both?
- What does the author think of both the doctors and the priests?

What kinds of questions will you get in the exam?

There are four main types of question that can be set on sources.

1 Questions about what sources say

These questions test how well you can work out what a source says. They can be asked in different ways, for example:

> What is the message of this source?

> What does the author think about . . .?

> What can you learn from this source about . . .?

> What impression does this source give of . . .?

> How far do these two sources agree?

REMEMBER

- Study the source carefully and go beyond its surface meaning.
- Explain your answer using details in the source.
- Your knowledge of the topic will help you work out what the source is saying and help you explain this in your answer.

- Only use knowledge in your answer if it helps you explain the meaning of the source. Do not tell the examiner everything you know about the topic for its own sake – they will not be impressed.
- Only do what the question asks and no more. This type of question does not ask you to say if you trust the source, so do not comment on this.

Go back to the answer you wrote to the question 'What message did the artist want to give about surgeons?'. This was about the drawing below showing a dissection. Compare your answer to the four opposite. Rate the answers (including yours) from 1 to 5, making 5 the best answer.

Student A

The artist is saying that the surgeons are horrible, nasty people. He does this by showing them carrying out a dissection. It shows that they are cruel and do not care what they are doing. I don't think the person who drew this liked surgeons at all.

Student B

The artist was trying to say that surgeons were horrible, cruel people. The poor patient who is being operated on is in great pain and the surgeons seem to be making a joke of the whole thing. You can see this by the look on their faces – they are enjoying it. One of the surgeons seems to be cutting the patient's eye out. This will not do him any good. Nor will the dog who is eating bits of the patient. The patient must be in great pain.

Student C

Although this drawing shows a dissection and not surgery it still gives a message about surgeons. Surgeons carried out dissections to find out more about the body and to train students. However, the artist has drawn lots of disgusting details to make surgeons look bad. You would think that they would have some respect for the corpse but they are letting a dog eat some of the innards. The whole thing looks like a piece of entertainment with people enjoying the dissection. The artist has the corpse sitting up a little to make it look as if it is alive. This was to play on the fears people had that surgeons sometimes dissected people who had not died on the scaffold and were still alive. All this was to make surgeons look as bad as possible.

Student D

People in those days did not think much of surgeons. They were often not trained as much as doctors and had developed from being barbers and were regarded by many people as no better than butchers because many people died after being operated on. In those days they did not have anaesthetics and people were in dreadful pain when they were operated on. Many died of shock, and others died of infection. All this gave surgeons a very bad reputation.

Examiner's comments

Answer D is the weakest answer because it completely ignores the source. It tells us quite a lot about surgeons, but it does not answer the question.

Answer B is also weak because it has misunderstood the source. The student who wrote it seems to think the drawing shows an operation! However, the student has used some of the details in the drawing to show how surgeons are shown as horrible and so some marks would be awarded.

Answer A is quite accurate on what the artist was trying to say about surgeons but the answer is not supported. To get good marks, answers should be supported by reference to details in the source and to some knowledge. This answer has neither.

Answer C is the best. Here the student does what Student A failed to do. He or she has supported their answer with reference to details in the source and to some knowledge. The details of the source have been used very well to explain the answer.

2 Questions about what you can work out from a source

These questions test whether you can use the source to work out things that go beyond what the source actually says. It is possible to work out from a source the following:

What the purpose of the artist/author was.

Why it was published at a particular time.

What kind of person might have produced the source, for example an opponent or a supporter of smallpox vaccination.

How people at the time might have reacted to the source.

Who the source was directed at (the intended audience).

Earlier, you wrote about the cartoon 'The Silent Highwayman' (page 5) and worked out why was it published in 1858.

Compare your answer to the two opposite. The good features of Answer A have been highlighted.

THE "SILENT HIGHWAY"-MAN.

"Your MONEY or your LIFE!"

Knowledge of people's beliefs about smells and bad air causing disease is used. It is linked to details in the cartoon, such as what the skeleton represents.

Straight to why 1858 – knowledge of the Great Stink used.

Purpose of cartoon explained – linked to explanation of what 'Your money or your life' means. More knowledge used to explain this and opposition to higher rates mentioned.

Answer A

This cartoon was published in 1858 because of the Great Stink. This took place in 1858 because it was a very hot summer and the sewerage in the River Thames sent a dreadful smell around London. Many people at that time believed that smells like this caused disease. The cartoon is showing people that the filthy state of the River Thames is responsible for disease spreading. This is shown by the dead animals in the water and by the skeleton which represents death. This means that death is coming from the river. The cartoon was published to make people aware of the dangers and to get them to do something about it. The phrase 'Your money or your life' is what the skeleton is saying to the people of London – if you will not pay taxes to clean things up you will pay with your life by catching disease. This is put in because many people did not want to pay higher rates.

Answer B

This cartoon was published in 1858 because of the outbreak of cholera in the 1850s. Just a few years before, John Snow had shown that cholera was spread by water polluted by sewage. Many sewers were emptied into the River Thames. This cartoon is warning people that there will be more outbreaks of cholera unless the River Thames is cleaned up. The dead animals represent the fact that the river is spreading disease. The skeleton, which represents death, is saying 'Your money or your life'. People were against paying taxes to have proper sewers and clean up the Thames. But the skeleton is warning them that if they don't, they will die from cholera.

The interesting thing about Answer B is that it concentrates on the outbreak of cholera in the 1850s and Snow's work on cholera. Answer A concentrates on the Great Stink. Both are acceptable because they both explain why the cartoon was published in the late 1850s.

Have a close look at Answer B. Does it:

- explain why the cartoon was published in 1858?
- explain the purpose of the cartoon?
- use details of the cartoon in its explanation?
- use some knowledge in its explanation?

Now ask these questions about the answer you wrote.

3 Questions asking you to evaluate sources

These questions sometimes ask you to evaluate sources for reliability, for example:

Do you trust what a source says?

If two sources disagree, does this mean one of them cannot be trusted?

Does the content of one source make another source reliable or unreliable?

Is one source more reliable than another?

and sometimes for usefulness, for example:

In what ways is a source useful to us with reference to a particular topic?

Is one source more useful than another?

Because a source is biased, does this mean it is of no use to us?

Here are some **do's** and **don'ts** when answering these types of question.

Reliability questions

Don't...

Claim that a source is reliable simply because of what type of source it is. For example, never write that a source is reliable because it was written at the time, or because it was written by an eye-witness, or because it was written by a vicar and all vicars can be trusted. Some sources written at the time can be trusted, others cannot. It all depends on the particular source in front of you and on what it says and why it was produced.

Do...

Look at what the source says, and at who wrote or drew it.

Check claims made in the source against your knowledge of the topic. This might help you decide if it can be trusted or not. Explain this fully, for example explain how knowledge that you have conflicts with claims made in the source.

Ask yourself – did the author or artist have any reason for writing or drawing what they did? Did they have a purpose, were they trying to influence the views of others, did they have something to cover up, or did they have something to gain? In other words, are there any reasons why you should be suspicious about what they are telling us? Sometimes you will know something about the author or artist, sometimes you will be told something about them (as you were about Lord Londonderry). Finally, make sure you explain your answer fully.

Usefulness questions

Don't...

Think that a source cannot be useful to you because it is biased. The fact that it is biased means it will tell you a lot about the person who wrote or drew it!

Assume that it is only useful for the obvious information it gives you.

Do...

Look at what the source says. The source will certainly tell you something about the views and purpose of the author or artist.

Look out for things the author or artist did not intend to tell us.

You answered a question earlier (page 9) about whether you trusted Lord Londonderry's letter. Here are three different answers to that question. Which is the best one, and what is wrong with the other two?

Student A

I trust Lord Londonderry because he was a very important man and he would know what was going on. He lived near Sunderland and so he should know what he is talking about when he writes about what was happening in Sunderland. He was there at the time and so what he says will be right.

Student B

I think Lord Londonderry is telling the truth when he says there is no real danger in Sunderland. I believe him because he says he is not going to move his family away and so he must think it is safe. Also Dr Brown said that cholera is not infectious. This means there is no danger of people catching it. Dr Brown should know because he is a doctor.

Student C

I do not trust Lord Londonderry. He is acting out of selfish motives. He wants the ban of ships going in and out of Sunderland to be lifted so he can send out the coal from his coalmines. The ban was probably costing him a lot of money if he couldn't sell his coal. I don't think Dr Brown's letter about cholera not being infectious means that Londonderry is telling the truth. Brown was an old friend of Londonderry. He was his doctor and needed to keep in favour with him because Londonderry was such an important man in the area. If he upset Londonderry he would be ruined. This means he would write anything Londonderry wanted him to. Londonderry simply wants the ban on ships lifted so he can sell his coal. He is being totally selfish and I do not trust him.

See if you agree with these comments.

Student A trusts what Lord Londonderry says simply because he lived there and was writing at the time. The student has ignored all the other things we know about Londonderry. The fact that Londonderry was there at the time does not mean he was telling the truth.

Student B's answer is a bit better because he or she does use some of the evidence in the source. The student argues that Londonderry wouldn't risk his family and so when he says it is safe in Sunderland and his family will stay there he is telling the truth. However, there are problems with this line of argument, for example Londonderry might be ready to risk his family to save his business. The student also uses what Dr Brown has to say – but can we trust him?

Student C has written the best answer. He or she has realised that Londonderry has reasons of his own to persuade everyone that there was no danger and that ships should be let back into Sunderland. The student also explains why what Dr Brown has written does not make Londonderry any more trustworthy. It is a good answer because it gets straight to the point, but it also explains, rather than just asserts. The only important point the student misses is that Londonderry might have sent his letter to a newspaper in London to try to put pressure on the government to lift the ban on ships in Sunderland.

4 Questions asking you to use all the sources to reach an overall conclusion

There is nearly always one of these questions at the end of the exam paper. You will find one at the end of most of the source investigations that come later in this book. Here is such a question from one of those investigations:

> Study all the sources. 'Mary Seacole and not Florence Nightingale deserves to be called the "The Angel of the Crimea".' How far do the sources convince you that this statement is right? Use the sources and your knowledge to explain your answer.

If you know what to do you can pick up a lot of marks in this question (it always carries more marks than any of the other questions).

Here is what to do:

1 You must base your answer on a discussion of the sources. Do not answer the question by ignoring the sources and writing down everything you know about Mary Seacole and Florence Nightingale.

2 Go through all the sources quickly and make a rough list of the sources that support the statement, and a list of those that disagree with the statement. You can list the sources by letter.

3 State which sources support the statement. Explain how they do this. Refer to any source you use by letter so the examiner knows which source you are using.

The three most important things you need to remember about answering source questions are:

- All the questions will be about the sources – you must base your answers on the sources.
- Use your knowledge in your answer, but only use it when it helps you to say something better about the sources. Do not put it in for its own sake.
- For every source, ask yourself – why was this source produced? What was the artist or the author trying to do?

Good luck with the exam. After doing all this you should find it easy!

4 State which sources disagree with the statement. Explain how they do this. Refer to the sources by letter.

5 You do not have to use all the sources, but you should use most of them.

6 To get full marks you have to show that some sources can or cannot be trusted, in other words you should evaluate some of them. For example there might be some sources that seem to support the statement but you do not trust them. This means they cannot really be used to support the statement. You need to explain why you do not trust them. This might mean repeating something you have written in an earlier answer – do not worry about this.

SOURCE INVESTIGATION 1

Were Hippocrates' ideas about medicine important?

Read all the sources, then answer the questions on page 20.

The ancient Greeks had many new ideas about the causes and treatments of illnesses. The Greek doctor Hippocrates, who lived sometime in the years between 460BC and 377BC, developed theories about why people fell ill and the sorts of treatment that would work best for them. Hippocrates and his followers trained many doctors who followed Hippocratic methods. But at the same time, the Greeks were taking their sick friends and relatives to Asclepions, where they believed Asclepius, the god of healing, would cure them. Does this mean that Hippocrates' ideas were not important?

● **SOURCE A**

A man came here with an abscess in his abdomen. When asleep in the Temple of Asclepius he had a dream. It seemed to him that the god ordered his servants to hold him tightly so that he could cut open his abdomen. The man tried to get away, but they gripped him and bound him. Asclepius cut his belly open, removed the abscess and, after having stitched him up again, released him from his bonds. He then walked out, but the floor was covered in blood.

Ambrosia of Athens became blind in one eye. She had always laughed at Asclepius' cures, but one night she dreamed he was standing beside her. He promised to make her eye better if she gave a silver pig to the Asclepion as a memorial to her ignorance. She agreed and he cut into her diseased eyeball and poured in some medicine. When she woke in the morning, she was cured.

Some of the inscriptions found carved into the wall of the Asclepion at Epidaurus. They record cures said to have happened in the Asclepion.

● **SOURCE B**

A Greek carving made in about 350BC, showing the god Asclepius curing a boy called Archinos.

WERE HIPPOCRATES' IDEAS ABOUT MEDICINE IMPORTANT? **19**

FROM PRE

FROM PREHISTORY TO THE ROMANS

FROM PREHISTORY TO THE ROMANS

FROM PREHISTORY TO THE ROMANS

OM PREHISTORY TO THE ROMANS

● SOURCE C

First we had to bathe Plutus in the sea. Then we went into the temple where we placed our offerings to the gods on the altar. There were many sick people present, with many kinds of illnesses. Soon the temple priest put out the light and told us all to go to sleep and not to speak, no matter what noises we heard. The god sat down by Plutus. First he wiped the patient's head, then with a cloth of clean linen he wiped Plutus' eyelids a number of times. Next, Panacea, the god's daughter, covered his face and head with a scarlet cloth. The god whistled and two huge snakes appeared and crept under the cloth and licked Plutus' eyelids. Then Plutus sat up. He could see again, but the god, his daughters and the serpents had disappeared.

From *Plutus*, a play written by Aristophanes around 400BC. Plutus had gone to the Asclepion to be cured of blindness.

● SOURCE D

Whoever intends to understand medicine must learn all that is written here. First he must consider the effects on the body of each of the seasons of the year and the differences between them. He must take note of the winds, cold or warm. In the same way, he must observe how men live, what they like, what they eat and what they drink, whether or not they take physical exercise or are idle and fat. All this a doctor must know, in order to understand illnesses and be in a position where he can prescribe suitable treatments for them.

From *On Airs, Waters and Places* written by Hippocrates.

● SOURCE E

In winter, people should eat as much as possible and drink as little as possible – wine, bread, roast meat and few vegetables. This will keep the body hot and dry. In summer they should drink more and eat less – watered wine, barley cakes and boiled meat – so that the body will stay cold and moist. Walking should be fast in winter and slow in summer.

From *A Programme for Health*, one of the books in the Hippocratic Collection.

● SOURCE F

After awakening, he should not arise at once but should wait until the heaviness of sleep has gone. After arising he should rub his whole body with oil. Then he should wash his face and eyes using pure water. He should rub his teeth inside and outside with the fingers using fine peppermint powder to get rid of remnants of food. He should clean nose and ears inside, preferably with well-perfumed oil. He should rub and anoint his head every day. Long walks before meals clear out the body, prepare it for receiving food and give it more power for digesting.

From a book by a Greek doctor, Diocles of Carystus, a follower of Hippocrates. He lived in Athens at around 390BC.

● **SOURCE G**

I swear by Apollo the physician and Asclepius and Hygeia and Panacea and all the gods and goddesses, that I will fulfil this oath.

- *I will use my power to help the sick to the best of my ability. I will not harm any man.*
- *I will not give a deadly drug to anyone. Neither will I help a woman to have an abortion.*
- *I will not use the knife, but will leave this to those men who do this work.*
- *Whenever I go into a house, I will go to help the sick and never with the intention of doing harm. I will not indulge in sexual relations with men or women.*
- *What I may see or hear, in the course of treating patients, I will keep secret.*

Part of the Hippocratic oath, sworn by all doctors trained in Hippocratic methods.

Questions

1 Study **Source A**.
What can we learn about medicine in ancient Greece from this source?
Use the source to explain your answer. [5]

2 Study **Sources A** and **B**.
Sources A and B agree about Asclepius. Does this mean they can be trusted?
Use the sources and your knowledge to explain your answer. [6]

3 Study **Source C**.
Plays are written to entertain people. Does this mean that this source is no use to historians?
Use the source and your knowledge to explain your answer. [7]

4 Study **Source D**.
Why do you think Hippocrates wrote this?
Use the source and your knowledge to explain your answer. [7]

5 Study **Sources E** and **F**.
Would all Greeks be able to benefit from Hippocratic medicine?
Use the sources and your knowledge to explain your answer. [7]

6 Study **Source G**.
Are you surprised that the Hippocratic oath refers to the gods?
Use the source and your knowledge to explain your answer. [8]

7 Study **all** the sources.
'Hippocrates' ideas about medicine were not important because the Greeks carried on believing that the gods caused and cured illnesses.'
How far do the sources support this statement?
Use the sources and your knowledge to explain your answer. [10]

Did the Romans simply copy the Greeks' medical ideas and methods?

Read all the sources, then answer the questions on page 23.

By 20BC, the Romans had overrun the countries surrounding the Mediterranean, including Greece. There were few doctors in Rome because the head of the household was supposed to be responsible for the health of his family. Gradually, Greek ideas about medicine spread to Rome and many wealthy Romans studied the writings of people like Hippocrates. The Greeks were thought of as being the people with specialised medical knowledge. However, because the Romans had conquered the Greeks, Greek doctors were not held in high regard. Nevertheless, the Romans seemed to use Greek ideas in their medicine. Did they do no more than copy the Greeks?

● **SOURCE A**

White of an egg can help heal wounds. Yolk of an egg boiled hard in vinegar and roasted with pepper strips stops diarrhoea. Nits can be removed by dog grease. Deafness can be cured by goose grease, with the juice of an onion and some garlic.

Written by Pliny in his book *Natural History* which was completed in AD77.

● **SOURCE B**

A drawing of a Roman coin that was made in the third century AD, showing different stages in treatments under the goddess Salus.

● **SOURCE C**

A drawing of an altar found in the English city of Chester. It was made for a Roman official, Titus, and is dedicated to the god Asclepius.

● **SOURCE D**

To the Holy God Asclepius and to Hygeia, Julius Saturnius set this up.

To the mighty Saviour gods I, Hermogenes, a doctor, set up this altar.

To Asclepius and Salus, for the welfare of the cavalry regiment.

Inscriptions from altars found at Overborough in Lancashire, at Chester and at Binchester in Co. Durham, made at the time of the Roman occupation.

● **SOURCE E**

The case of the Emperor Aurelius was quite wonderful. A messenger brought me to the Emperor. Three doctors had watched him since dawn, they had felt his pulse and thought it was the beginning of fever. The Emperor asked me to feel his pulse. It seemed to me that his pulse, compared with the normal, was far from showing the onset of fever. My impression was that his stomach was overloaded with cold food, and that the food had turned into slimy excrement. The Emperor praised my diagnosis three times and said, 'That is it. I have eaten too much cold food.' From this time he never stopped praising me. 'He is the First of Doctors,' he said.

He then asked me what he should take. I replied that I knew of a similar case and said, 'I would usually prescribe wine with a little pepper.'

Written by Galen sometime after AD169.

● **SOURCE F**

I have done as much for medicine as Trajan did for the Roman Empire when he built bridges and roads through Italy. It is I, and I alone, who has revealed the true path of medicine. It must be admitted that Hippocrates already staked out this path. He prepared the way but I have made it passable.

Written by Galen in the AD170s.

● **SOURCE G**

There is no doubt that Greek doctors hunt for popularity. Medicine changes every day and we are swept along on the puffs of the clever brains of the Greeks. Of all the Greek ideas, it is only medicine that we Romans have not yet taken up. But it is not the practice of Greek medicine which we object to, but the doctors themselves. We dare not trust them. First they make their patients go without food and then they stuff them with food several times a day. Look at their diets and their ointments! These Greeks are plotting to kill us with their potions. I forbid you to have anything to do with them.

Written by Pliny in his book *Natural History* which was completed in AD77.

DID THE ROMANS SIMPLY COPY THE GREEKS' MEDICAL IDEAS AND METHODS? 23

FROM PREHISTORY TO THE ROMANS · FROM PREHISTORY TO THE ROMANS · FROM PREHISTORY TO THE ROMANS · FROM PREHISTORY TO THE ROMANS

● **SOURCE H**

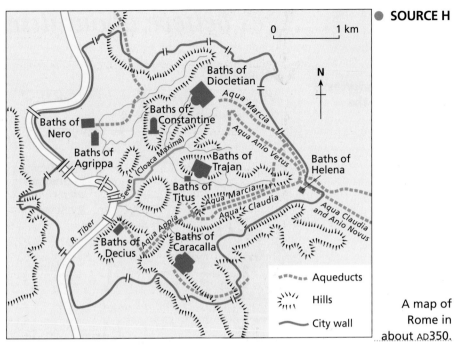

A map of Rome in about AD350.

Questions

1 Study **Sources A** and **B**.
What can you learn from these sources about the ways in which Romans treated sick people?
Use the sources to explain your answer. [7]

2 Study **Sources C** and **D**.
Do these sources prove that Greek ideas about medicine were used in the Roman Empire?
Use the sources and your knowledge to explain your answer. [7]

3 Study **Source E**.
'This source shows that Galen had no new ideas about the causes or the treatment of disease.'
Use the source and your knowledge to explain whether or not you agree with this statement. [8]

4 Study **Sources E, F** and **G**.
Are you surprised by what Pliny says in Source G?
Use the sources and your knowledge to explain your answer. [8]

5 Study **Source H**.
What does this source tell you about Roman attitudes towards medicine?
Use the source and your knowledge to explain your answer. [8]

6 Study **all** the sources.
'The Romans simply copied Greek medical ideas and methods.' How far do the sources convince you that this statement is right?
Use the sources and your knowledge to explain your answer. [12]

What did people in the Middle Ages believe about disease?

SOURCE INVESTIGATION 3

Read all the sources, then answer the questions on page 26.

● **SOURCE A**

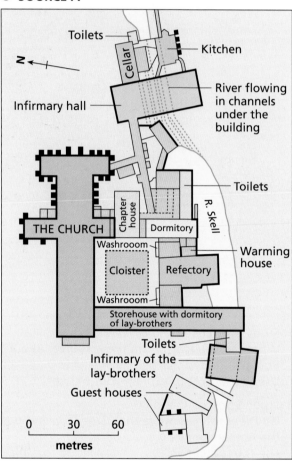

A plan of Fountains Abbey, near Ripon in Yorkshire, built in the Middle Ages.

● **SOURCE B**

Write these words on the jaw of the patient. 'In the name of the Father, Son and Holy Ghost, Amen.' The pain will stop at once as I have often seen.

A fourteenth-century charm for curing toothache used by John of Gaddesden, a leading medieval doctor.

● **SOURCE C**

A drawing from the fifteenth century showing doctors testing samples of patients' blood for taste, smell and heat.

● **SOURCE D**

A drawing from the thirteenth century showing King Edward the Confessor (who died in 1066) touching people with the skin disease scrofula.

● **SOURCE E**

A drawing from the thirteenth century showing a doctor making a patient vomit.

● **SOURCE F**

A drawing from the thirteenth century showing Hippocrates treating a patient. Hippocrates is shown in medieval dress.

● **SOURCE G**

I forbid you ever to enter churches, or go into a market, or a bakehouse, or any groups of people.
I forbid you ever to wash your hands or even any of your belongings in spring or stream water.
I forbid you to go out without your leper's dress.
I forbid you to have intercourse with any woman except your wife.
I forbid you to touch infants or young folk.

From thirteenth-century rules for lepers.

● **SOURCE H**

A drawing from the fourteenth century showing a pharmacy attached to a doctor's surgery.

● **SOURCE I**

They gather by the hundreds at the house of the blood-letter. After he draws their blood he tells them, in order to gain an extra fee, that he sees by their blood that they will need another blood-letting. And the fools return.

From a medieval guide for doctors.

Questions

1 Study **Source A**.
How far does this source show that people in the Middle Ages realised the importance of public health?
Use the source and your knowledge to explain your answer. [6]

2 Study **Source B**.
Why did people use treatments like this one in the Middle Ages?
Use the source and your knowledge to explain your answer. [6]

3 Study **Sources C, D** and **E**.
How similar are the ideas in these three sources?
Use the sources and your knowledge to explain your answer. [8]

4 Study **Source F**.
Are you surprised to see Hippocrates being shown as a medieval doctor?
Use the source and your knowledge to explain your answer. [7]

5 Study **Sources G** and **H**.
What can you learn from these two sources about medieval medicine?
Use the sources to explain your answer. [6]

6 Study **Source I**.
If blood-letters were so bad why was bloodletting so popular in the Middle Ages?
Use the source and your knowledge to explain your answer. [7]

7 Which one of these three statements is best supported by these sources?
'In the Middle Ages they had supernatural beliefs about the causes and cures of disease.'
'In the Middle Ages they believed disease had natural causes and cures.'
'In the Middle Ages natural and supernatural beliefs about medicine existed side by side.'
Use the sources and your knowledge to explain your answer. [10]

SOURCE INVESTIGATION 4

How far were medieval attempts to prevent the plague a waste of time?

Read all the sources, then answer the questions on page 29.

The Black Death arrived in Europe in 1347 and hit England the following year, killing over 40 per cent of the population. This devastating plague spread rapidly, attacking towns and ports, villages and farms. It left as quickly as it came, but returned again and again over the following 300 years. The plague struck rich and poor alike, killing swiftly and painfully. No one at the time knew how it spread, or what caused it.

● **SOURCE A**

To the Lord Mayor of London
An order: to cause the human waste and other filth lying in the streets and lanes in the city and its suburbs to be removed with all speed. Also to cause the city and suburbs to be kept clean, as it used to be in the time of the previous mayors. This is so that no greater cause of death may arise from such smells. The King has learned that the city and suburbs are so full with the filth from out of the houses by day and night that the air is infected and the city poisoned. This is a danger to men, especially by the contagious sickness which increases daily.

Part of a letter from King Edward III to the Lord Mayor of London, 1349.

● **SOURCE B**

In 1349, over six hundred men came to London from Flanders. Sometimes at St Paul's Cathedral and sometimes at other points in the city, they made two daily public appearances wearing clothes from the thighs to the ankle but otherwise stripped bare. Each wore a cap with a red cross in front and behind. Each had in his right hand a whip with three tails. Each tail had a knot and through the middle of it there were sometimes sharp nails fixed. They marched naked in a file one behind the other and whipped themselves on their naked and bleeding bodies. Four of them would chant in their native tongues and four would chant in response. Each of them in turn would step over the others and give one stroke with his whip to the man lying under him.

Robert of Avesbury, who lived in London at the time, describes the flagellants.

● **SOURCE C**

A painting from the 1300s of flagellants whipping themselves.

● **SOURCE D**

Terrible is God towards men. He often allows plagues, miserable famines, conflicts, wars and other forms of suffering to arise, and uses them to terrify and torment men and so drive out their sins.

Part of a letter from the prior of the abbey of Christchurch, Canterbury, Kent to the bishop of London on 28 September 1348.

● **SOURCE E**

Whatever the people say, the truth is that there were two causes of the plague, one general and one particular. The general cause was the close position of the three great planets, Saturn, Jupiter and Mars. This had taken place in 1345 on 24 March in the 14th degree of Aquarius. Such a coming together of planets is always a sign of wonderful, terrible or violent things to come. The particular cause of the disease in each person was the state of the body – bad digestion, weakness and blockage, and for this reason, people died.

From *On Surgery*, a book written by a French doctor, Guy de Chauliac, in 1365. He was one of the most famous doctors of the 1300s.

● **SOURCE F**

First you should avoid too much eating and drinking and also avoid baths which open the pores, for the pores are the doorways through which poisonous air can enter the body. In cold or rainy weather, you should light fires in your room, and in foggy or windy weather you should inhale perfumes every morning before leaving home.

If, however, the plague occurs during hot weather, you must eat cold things rather than hot and also drink more than you eat. Make little use of hot substances such as pepper, garlic and onions.

Advice written by John of Burgundy in 1365 on how to avoid the plague. He wrote one of the first books about the plague.

● **SOURCE G**

A fourteenth-century German drawing showing Jews being burned. They were blamed by many people at the time for spreading the plague.

● **SOURCE H**

Many people thought that to get rid of the plague it was necessary to break up the air. Various ways of doing this were tried. Church bells were rung and muskets were fired. Many people kept canaries in their rooms to fly about and keep the air moving. It was also thought that speckled spiders, lizards and toads would purify the polluted air and absorb the poison which had been brought in by the plague.

From *The Black Death*, edited by J Nohl, 1961.

Questions

1 Study **Source A**.
   What can you learn from Source A about public health in the 1300s?
   Use the source to explain your answer. [6]

2 Study **Sources B** and **C**.
   How far does Source C prove that Source B was an accurate description of the flagellants?
   Use the sources and your knowledge to explain your answer. [8]

3 Study **Sources D** and **E**.
   How far do these two sources agree about the causes of the plague?
   Use the sources and your knowledge to explain your answer. [8]

4 Study **Source F**.
   Are you surprised by the methods being used in Source F?
   Use the source and your knowledge to explain your answer. [8]

5 Study **Sources G** and **H**.
   'These two sources show people did not have any understanding of the causes of the plague.' How far do you agree with this statement?
   Use the sources and your knowledge to explain your answer. [8]

6 Study **all** the sources.
   'Medieval attempts to stop the plague spreading were useless.'
   How far do the sources support this view?
   Use the sources and your knowledge to explain your answer. [12]

SOURCE
INVESTIGATION

Ambroise Paré: why did he make his discoveries when he did?

Read all the sources,
then answer the
questions on
page 33.

Ambroise Paré (1510–90) learned his craft in a practical way as an apprentice to a barber surgeon. He later gained more practical experience as an army surgeon – France was, at that time, involved in a great many wars. He served with the army for twenty years. Despite the fact that Paré did not go to university and achieve proper qualifications he later became a successful surgeon in Paris. How far was his success due to his own skill?

● **SOURCE A**

This painting of barber surgeons was done c. 1556 by Pieter Brueghel.

● **SOURCE B**

Eventually I ran out of oil. I was forced instead to use an ointment made from yolks of eggs, oil of roses and turpentine. That night I could not sleep, fearing what would happen because the wounds were not cauterised and that I should find those on whom I had not used the burning oil dead or poisoned. To my surprise, I found those to whom I gave my ointment feeling little pain, and their wounds without swelling, having rested reasonably well during the night. Whereas the others, on whom I had used the boiling oil, were feverish, with great pain and swelling about the edges of their wounds. And then I decided never to cruelly burn poor men wounded with gunshot.

Ambroise Paré describes what happened when he was treating gunshot wounds in 1537. He published this account in 1545.

● SOURCE C

When you have cut off and taken away the arm or leg or foot, let the wound bleed a little, according to the strength of the patient. Then let the veins and arteries be tied up as speedily as you can so that the course of the flowing blood may be stopped.

I used to stop the bleeding in another way, of which I am ashamed. I had observed my masters whose methods I intended to follow. They had various hot irons and boiling oil which they used on the stump. This kind of treatment brought great and tormenting pain to the patient. And truly, of those that were burnt, a third did not recover.

I must earnestly entreat all surgeons to leave this old and too cruel way of healing, and embrace this new way. I believe it was taught to me by a special favour of God, for I did not learn it from my masters, neither have I at any time found it used by anyone else.

From *On Amputations* by Ambroise Paré, published in 1575.

● SOURCE D

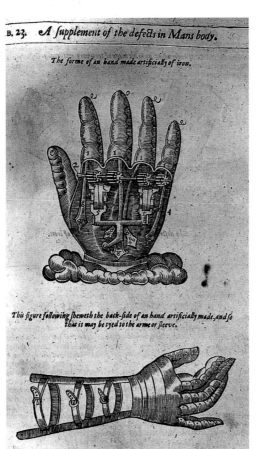
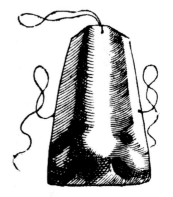

These pictures of artificial hands and noses are from *Ten Books on Surgery* by Ambroise Paré, published in 1575.

● **SOURCE E**

How dare you say you will teach me surgery, you who have never come out of your study? Surgery is learned by the eye and the hands. I can perform surgical operations which you cannot do, because you have never left your study. Diseases are not to be cured by talking, but by proper treatment. You, my little master, know nothing else than how to chatter in a chair.

From *The Apology and Treatise of Ambroise Paré*, published in 1585. Here Paré is attacking the Head of the Faculty of Physicians in Paris (France's most powerful medical organisation), who had criticised him for not asking for the Faculty's permission to publish his work.

● **SOURCE F**

In this fortunate age, anatomy, like every other area of medical study, has begun to revive and raise its head from the dark depths.

From *The Fabric of the Human Body* by Vesalius, 1543.

● **SOURCE G**

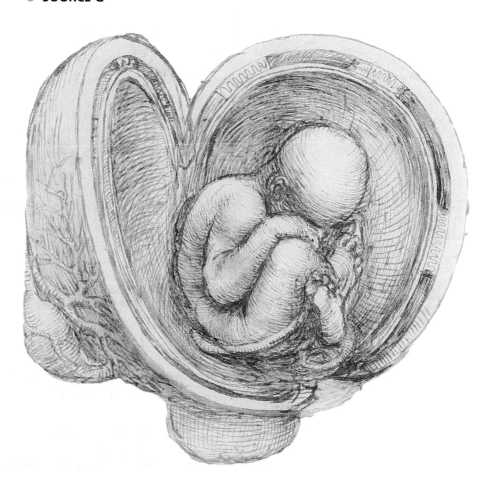

Leonardo da Vinci's drawing of a foetus in the womb, 1510.

● **SOURCE H**

Ambroise Paré, who started as a barber surgeon, was the man who would renew and reform surgery. He became personal surgeon to three French kings. His reputation was so great that he was made a member of the important College of Surgery – a very unusual achievement for somebody like Paré who had not been to university. He was the greatest surgeon of his time.

A recent description of Paré.

● **SOURCE I**

Within two generations of Paré, French surgeons had returned to old methods and French surgery was at as low a level as it had been before Paré. This was because of opposition to change by the Faculty of Physicians in Paris. There were also practical problems with using Paré's methods. No fewer than fifty-three ligatures were necessary in a thigh amputation. As a result, ligatures could only come into general use after a method had been found to control the flow of blood until the surgeon could tie the blood vessels.

A recent description of French surgery after Paré.

Questions

1 Study **Source A**.
   What did the artist of Source A think of barber surgeons?
   Use the source to explain your answer. [6]

2 Study **Sources B** and **C**.
   How similar are these two accounts?
   Use the sources and your knowledge to explain your answer. [6]

3 Study **Sources C** and **D**.
   Which source would be the more useful to a historian investigating Paré's work?
   Use the sources and your knowledge to explain your answer. [7]

4 Study **Source E**.
   Are you surprised Paré wrote this?
   Use the source and your knowledge to explain your answer. [7]

5 Study **Sources F** and **G**.
   Was it complete chance that Paré and Vesalius were making discoveries at the same time?
   Use the sources and your knowledge to explain your answer. [7]

6 Study **Sources H** and **I**.
   'One of these two sources must be wrong.' Do you agree?
   Use the sources and your own knowledge to explain your answer. [7]

7 Study **all** the sources.
   How far do these sources convince you that Paré's discoveries were made only because of his own skill?
   Use the sources and your own knowledge to explain your answer. [10]

Were quacks any worse than doctors?

Read all the sources, then answer the questions on page 37.

During the seventeenth, eighteenth and early nineteenth centuries, ordinary doctors and surgeons lost a lot of business to quacks. Quacks were often unqualified and sold their own medicines and pills which were made from secret ingredients and claimed to cure anything. Some of the quacks travelled around the country selling their medicines from portable stages which they set up in the street. They often used a clown and a monkey in their act.

Ordinary doctors claimed that quacks were not trained, they did not know what they were doing and their medicines were useless. In other words, the quacks were conmen. But were quacks really that bad? Were the doctors just as bad as the quacks?

● SOURCE A

1 Never trust those who pretend that the good of mankind is their only reason for offering their medicine for sale.

2 Conclude the advertiser to be a fool, who pretends that his medicine will cure different illnesses which have no connection to each other.

3 Do not believe lists of cases where the medicine is said to have worked, these are usually invented by the quack.

A list of rules for identifying quacks, written by a doctor in 1767.

● SOURCE B

The posts of houses and corners of streets were plastered over with doctors' posters and advertisements of ignorant fellows; quacking in medicine, and inviting people to come to them for remedies. These posters were full of phrases such as 'INFALLIBLE preventive Pills against the Plague', 'NEVER FAILING Preservatives against Infection', 'The ONLY-TRUE Plague-Water'.

A description written in 1722 about advertisements displayed in the streets of London in 1655.

● SOURCE C

The patients are informed that the doctor has thirteen lords and dukes with him that morning. Presently he enters; there is a general distribution of snuff, which, he assures them, is a cure for all diseases. When the people remind him of his advertisements of free treatment he replies that he charges fees so that he can supply medicines to the poor. To one woman who says she has no money, he answers that it makes no difference at all, but he happens to be very busy that morning.

An eye-witness description of the quack John Taylor in 1740.

● **SOURCE D**

My wife walked to Whitesmith to see a quack perform wonders. He has a stage built there and comes once a week to swindle poor deluded creatures out of their money. He sells packets which are to cure people of more illnesses than they ever had in their lives for one shilling each, by which means he takes £9 a day.

From the diary of Thomas Turner, a Sussex grocer, written in July 1760.

● **SOURCE E**

I was at Tunbridge in 1748, where I met with Taylor the famous quack. He seems to understand the anatomy of the eye perfectly well; he has a fine hand and good instruments, and performs all his operations with great skill.

A description of John Taylor by a doctor in 1748.

● **SOURCE F**

A cartoon, published in 1830, showing the quack John St John Long advertising his cures.

● **SOURCE G**

A drawing about the effects of quack pills, published in the early nineteenth century. The caption reads: 'This here Board is a hexact representation of me as I vos afore I took to Morrisons Pills and only took 480 boxes!! I lived on nothink else for a vortnight.'

● **SOURCE H**

A cartoon from 1736 entitled 'The Company of Undertakers', showing quacks and doctors. The quacks are the three at the top (John Taylor is the one on the left). The tops of doctors' canes contained perfume which was meant to protect them from infection. Here they are drawn to look like the batons which were used by undertakers when conducting funerals. The words at the bottom mean 'Everywhere the image of death'.

● **SOURCE I**

The difference between a Real Doctor and a Quack-Pretender is this, that the first is careful and cautious in all doubtful cases; the latter is rash and inconsiderate in everything he does, his ignorance makes him daring, and he always promises total success.

Written by a doctor at the end of the seventeenth century.

● **SOURCE J**

So many Doctors, Quacks, Surgeons, and Apothecaries are the Enemies of good health. It is indeed often asked, what Disease a Man died of, but really the Question should be what Doctor did he die of. Illnesses seize men, but the Doctors execute them. Never read a doctor's prescription – it is a passport into the next world.

From a magazine published in 1710.

Questions

1 Study **Sources A**, **B** and **C**.
How far do these sources agree about quacks?
Use the sources to explain your answer.   [7]

2 Study **Source D**.
Do you think the author of Source D approved of quacks?
Use the source to explain your answer.   [6]

3 Study **Sources C** and **E**.
Do you trust the description of John Taylor in Source E?
Use the sources and your knowledge to explain your answer.   [7]

4 Study **Source F**.
Why do you think this cartoon was published?
Use the source and your knowledge to explain your answer.   [7]

5 Study **Source G**.
Does this source provide reliable historical evidence?
Use the source and your knowledge to explain your answer.   [6]

6 Study **Sources H**, **I** and **J**.
Would the author of Source I or the author of Source J have agreed
with the cartoon (Source H)?
Use the sources to explain your answer.   [7]

7 Study **all** the sources.
Do these sources show that quacks were worse than doctors?
Use the sources and your knowledge to explain your answer.   [10]

SOURCE INVESTIGATION

Why did so many people oppose vaccination?

Read all the sources, then answer the questions on page 41.

Smallpox was the most feared disease in eighteenth-century Britain. Not only were thousands killed every year but those that survived were left with terrible scars. Edward Jenner (1749–1823) was a country doctor who began working in Berkeley, Gloucestershire, in 1773. He became interested in local stories about cowpox, a mild disease caught by dairymaids from the cows they milked. He made careful observations and kept accurate notes on what he observed. He found that the dairymaids who caught cowpox rarely caught smallpox. Eventually, Jenner discovered that people could be protected from smallpox if they were injected with a small amount of cowpox. He didn't know why this worked, but it did. Thousands of people were saved from death and disfigurement. But many opposed the whole idea of vaccination and poured scorn on Jenner's work. Why?

● SOURCE A

The smallpox here is entirely harmless. Every autumn people send to each other to ask if any of their family has a mind to have the smallpox. They make children's parties for this. An old woman comes with a shell full of the pus of the best smallpox and asks what vein you would like to have opened. She immediately rips open, with a large needle, the one you select. She puts into the vein as much smallpox pus as can lie on the head of the needle, and afterwards binds up the wound. The children play together all the rest of the day and are in perfect health for eight days. Then the fever begins, and they keep to their beds two days, very seldom three. They have rarely above 20 or 30 spots on their faces, which never mark permanently. In eight days' time, they are as well as before the illness. Every year, thousands undergo this operation.

I should write about it to some of our doctors in England if I knew one of them that I thought would be willing to give up a considerable amount of their income to do this for the good of mankind.

From a letter written by Lady Mary Wortley Montague while she was living in Turkey in 1717, to to one of her friends in England. She is describing inoculation.

● SOURCE B

Case 16
Sarah Nelmes, a dairymaid near this place, was infected with the cowpox from her master's cows in May 1796. A large sore and the usual symptoms were produced.

Case 17
James Phipps. I selected a healthy boy, about eight years old. The pus was taken from the cowpox sore on the hand of Sarah Nelmes and it was inserted on 14 May 1796 into the arm of the boy by two cuts each about half an inch long. On the seventh day he complained of uneasiness, on the ninth he became a little chilly, lost his appetite and had a slight headache and spent the night with some degree of restlessness, but on the following day he was perfectly well.

In order to prove that the boy was safe from the smallpox, he was inoculated with smallpox matter, but no disease followed. Several months later he was again inoculated with smallpox matter but again no disease followed.

. . . And thus it is concluded that the cowpox protects the human body from the infection of the smallpox.

Extracts from Edward Jenner's casebook from 1796, published in 1798. He is describing vaccination.

● **SOURCE C**

1791

March 7   *The smallpox spreads very much in the parish. Abigail Robert's husband was very bad with it in the natural way. His children are inoculated by Johnny Reeve, as are also Richmond's children near me. It is a pity that all the poor in the parish were not inoculated also. I am entirely for it.*

An extract from the diary of James Woodforde (1740–1803). He was a vicar who spent his working life in Norfolk and Somerset. He is describing inoculation using smallpox matter.

● **SOURCE D**

The Suttons in eleven years inoculated 2514 people, for large fees. They also sold, for anything between fifty and a hundred pounds, to doctors living far away from them, the secrets of their methods. They had their own inoculation house in Ingatestone in Essex where patients were prepared for the operation and rested after it.

An account of the Sutton family business. They inoculated people with smallpox matter in the 1760s and 1770s. This extract is from a book published in 1959.

● **SOURCE E**

The number of the poor who accepted free vaccination from organisations set up for that purpose remained very low. They were worried by the eruptions that took place in the skin of people who were vaccinated. The first reports of vaccination in London, and the accompanying eruptions, caused terror. This was made worse by the fact that Jenner could not explain why vaccination was not successful every time. Some people caught smallpox after they had been vaccinated. Anti-vaccinists claimed that smallpox inoculation could not fail because it was not possible to contract smallpox twice. They also claimed that there was no danger from smallpox because it came from God.

A recent description of events in 1800.

● **SOURCE F**

Only when compulsion combined with the self-interest of the rich and powerful did matters improve. In 1800, on the orders of the Earl of Lonsdale who had a linen factory in the village of Lowther, Dr Thornton vaccinated all 400 inhabitants. The smallpox did not spread. He completed about a thousand vaccinations in the neighbourhood within a few weeks.

From a book about Jenner published in 1991.

● **SOURCE G**

This cartoon is called 'The Cow-pock – or – The Wonderful Effects of the new Inoculation. The publication of the Anti-Vaccine Society'. It was published in 1802.

● **SOURCE H**

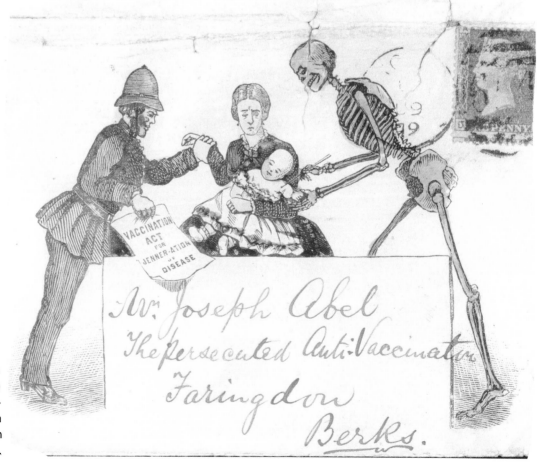

Vaccination has only the evidence of failures—proofs of a gross delusion and fraud. Small-pox is a process of cleansing. Vaccination is a process of corruption and death. One comes from God, a remedy for wrong—the other is a wrong to deceive and get plunder. The deceiver, of parents and the slayer of infants is the vaccinating doctor—his stock in trade filth and a lancet.

An envelope used by the Anti-Vaccination Society in 1899.

Questions

1 Study **Source A**.
Why do you think Lady Mary Wortley Montague wrote this letter in 1717?
Use the source and your knowledge to explain your answer. [5]

2 Study **Sources A** and **B**.
How similar are the methods described in Sources A and B?
Use the sources and your knowledge to explain your answer. [7]

3 Study **Sources C** and **D**.
Would James Woodforde and the Suttons have reacted to Jenner's vaccination in the same way?
Use the sources and your knowledge to explain your answer. [6]

4 Study **Sources E** and **F**.
Does Source F prove that the fears described in Source E were overcome?
Use the sources and your knowledge to explain your answer. [7]

5 Study **Source G**.
Why was this cartoon published in 1802?
Use the source and your knowledge to explain your answer. [7]

6 Study **Source H**.
Is it more surprising that people were opposing vaccination in 1899 than in 1799?
Use the source and your knowledge to explain your answer. [8]

7 Study **all** the sources.
'People opposed vaccination because they thought inoculation was safer.' How far do the sources support this view?
Use the sources and your knowledge to explain your answer. [10]

SOURCE INVESTIGATION 8

The body-snatchers

Read all the sources, then answer the questions on page 45.

In the early nineteenth century there was an ever-growing demand for corpses for dissection. Anatomists wanted to use them with their students who were training to be doctors. The only corpses that could be used legally for dissection were the bodies of murderers who had been sentenced to be dissected after they were hanged. Dissection was regarded by most people as a fate worse than death and judges used it as a punishment for the very worst murderers. These official dissections were carried out by the Company of Surgeons.

However, there were also many unofficial and illegal dissections. One of the most famous anatomists was Dr Knox of Edinburgh University. He bought corpses from body-snatchers who robbed new graves and sold on the corpses. Two men, Burke and Hare, who had provided Knox with many bodies, found an easier way of obtaining them. They suffocated people who stayed at Hare's boarding house. In 1828, when Mary Docherty became their sixteenth victim, they sold her body to Knox. However, they were arrested when one of Knox's students recognised her. Hare gave evidence against Burke who was hanged. His body was dissected in public and his skin sold in strips.

● **SOURCE A**

Behold the Villain's dire disgrace! Not Death itself can end.

An engraving from 1751 called 'The Reward of Cruelty'. It shows an official dissection by the Company of Surgeons.

● **SOURCE B**

Everyone, even doctors, shudders at the idea that the remains of all that was dear to him, a beloved parent, wife, sister or daughter, may be exposed to the rude gaze of unfeeling men, and afterwards be mutilated in the presence of hundreds of spectators.

From a book written in 1825. It described popular attitudes towards public dissection

● **SOURCE C**

The time chosen in the dark winter nights was between 6 and 8 o'clock. At 8 o'clock the churchyard watch began and the police started their rounds. The body-snatchers worked in small gangs, to allow at least one person to be on the lookout. Canvas would be laid by the grave for the displaced earth, so as to leave none on the surrounding grass. The digging was done with dagger-shaped spades. They were made of wood to avoid the clicking noise of iron striking stones. Part of the coffin lid was broken off to allow the body to be dragged out. Sacking was used to deaden the sound of the cracking wood. The whole process was completed in an hour because newly dug graves were used and so the soil was loose.

A medical professor at Edinburgh University in the 1820s describing how body-snatchers worked.

● **SOURCE D**

A nineteenth-century drawing of body-snatchers at work.

● **SOURCE E**

Name	Previous life	Later life
Butler	Porter in a dissecting room	A dealer in bones, sentenced to death for a mail-coach robbery.
Ben Crouch	Son of a Guy's Hospital carpenter	Bought a hotel in Margate but it failed when people knew where he had got his money from. He later became involved with thieves and died in poverty.
Bill Holmes	A gravedigger, he lost his job because he helped body-snatchers	Worked in a coach business, he later lived in poverty.
William Millard	Superintendent of St Thomas' Hospital dissecting room	Bought a restaurant but it failed. Died in prison after he was caught body-snatching.
Vaughan	A stonemason's labourer	Transported for theft of clothes from graves.

Details of London body-snatchers in the early nineteenth century, showing their lives before and after they became body-snatchers.

● **SOURCE F**

On Friday evening I met a man who asked me where he could get a pair of shoes mended. Being a shoemaker I took him home. The man asked if he could leave a box in the house. I agreed. After the man had left I looked in the box and saw a dead body. I left the body there.

On Saturday morning I met Mary Docherty. She said she had not eaten for twenty-four hours. I took her home and gave her breakfast. She sat by the fire until about three in the afternoon when she said she would go out to the New Town to beg for some food. She promised me she would return but she did not and I did not see her again. When I saw the dead body in the Police Office I thought it was the body under the bed but it was not Mary Docherty.

From Burke's statement on 3 November, 1828 after he had been arrested by the police for the murder of Mary Docherty.

● **SOURCE G**

An old woman of the name of Campbell came to Edinburgh some days ago. She took up lodgings in the house of a man named Burt or Burke. The old woman was to sleep on straw alongside Burke's bed. During the night shrieks were heard; but the neighbours paid no attention as such sounds were not unusual in the house. In the morning a female went into Burke's room and saw the old woman lying as if dead, some of the straw over her. She did not say anything, or raise any alarm. By the evening the body had been removed and, it was suspected, sold to be used in a public dissection.

From an Edinburgh newspaper, 3 November 1828.

● **SOURCE H**

Two body-snatchers had been arrested, and whilst being taken to prison had been torn from the constable by a crowd of the roughest sort of men, who dragged them by their legs along the muddy and stony road. They were covered from head to foot with mud, and their faces were bleeding from having been kicked.

An eyewitness account of events in Cambridge in 1830.

● **SOURCE I**

There was usually a race between the relatives and the students. The former to carry off the body complete, the latter to dissect it. As a result dissection was often performed in haste. It was not uncommon for the dissection to begin with the body still warm, the limbs not yet rigid and the blood fluid. I remember one occasion when the blood gushed from the first cut made in the skin.

From the memoirs of a surgeon at St Bartholomew's Hospital in the 1820s.

Questions

1 Study **Source A**.
   What did the artist of Source A think about dissection?
   Use the source and your knowledge to explain your answer. [7]

2 Study **Source B**.
   Source B was written hundreds of years after Vesalius started to dissect bodies. Are you surprised by the attitude towards dissection shown in this source?
   Use the source and your knowledge to explain your answer. [9]

3 Study **Sources C** and **D**.
   How far do these two sources agree about body-snatchers?
   Use the sources to explain your answer. [8]

4 Study **Source E**.
   What does this source tell you about body-snatchers?
   Use the source to explain your answer. [8]

5 Study **Sources F** and **G**.
   Do you think Burke was lying in Source F?
   Use the sources and your knowledge to explain your answer. [8]

6 Study **Sources H** and **I**.
   Would the author of Source I have approved of the events in Source H?
   Use the sources and your knowledge to explain your answer. [10]

How important was John Snow in the fight against cholera?

Read all the sources,
then answer the
questions on
page 49.

Cholera hit Britain in four massive epidemics in 1831–2, 1848–9, 1853–4 and 1866–7, killing over 125,000 people. There were many theories as to what caused cholera and many so-called 'cures' were offered to the public. In 1854 John Snow, a young doctor working in London, came up with one theory based on research of the area around Broad Street in Soho, London. He claimed this theory was supported by scientific proof. But has he been given too much credit for this? After all, it was not until 1861 that Pasteur published his theory that germs cause disease, and not until 1884 that Robert Koch discovered the germ that caused cholera.

● **SOURCE A**

A cartoon called 'A Court For King Cholera', published in 1852.

● **SOURCE B**

Sir

May we beg for your protection and power? We are, Sir, living in a wilderness so far as the rest of London knows anything of us. The rich and great people do not care about us. We live in muck and filth. We ain't got no privies, no dust bins, no drains, no water supplies, and no drain or sewer in the whole place. The Sewer Company, in Greek St., Soho Square, all great, rich, powerful men take no notice whatsoever of our complaints. The stench of a gulley-hole is disgusting. We all of us suffer, and numbers are ill, and if the cholera comes, Lord help us.

A letter in *The Times* in 1849, referring to the Broad Street area, Soho, London.

● SOURCE C

Within two hundred and fifty yards of the water pump in Broad Street, there were upwards of five hundred fatal attacks of cholera in ten days. There were only ten deaths in houses situated nearer another street pump. In five of these cases, the families of the deceased persons informed me that they always used the pump in Broad Street. In three other cases, the deceased were children who went to the school near the pump in Broad Street.

There is a brewery in Broad Street, near to the pump. Mr Huggins, the owner, informed me that there were more than seventy workmen employed in the brewery, and that none of them had suffered from the cholera. The men were allowed to drink beer and Mr Huggins believes they do not drink water at all. He is quite certain they never obtained water from the pump in the street.

There had been deaths from cholera just before the great outbreak not far from this well-pump, and human waste might, of course, be amongst the impurities finding their way into the water.

Part of John Snow's report on the causes of cholera, published in 1854.

● SOURCE D

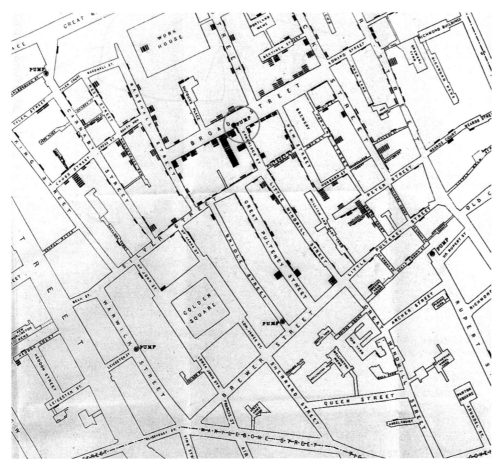

In August 1854, cholera cases began to appear in Soho, London. John Snow marked on a map the number of cholera cases and the position of the local water pumps. This is his map of the area around Broad Street, Soho. Each short black line represents a person who died; several lines together indicate many people from the same household.

● **SOURCE E**

If the Broad Street pump did actually become a source of disease, we believe that this may have been because its impure waters had soaked up the atmospheric infection [bad air] of the district. On the evidence, it seems impossible to doubt that the geographical distribution of cholera in London belongs more to the air than to the water.

From *The Report of the Committee for Scientific Enquiry into the Recent Cholera Epidemic,* published in 1855.

● **SOURCE F**

DEATH'S DISPENSARY.
OPEN TO THE POOR, GRATIS, BY PERMISSION OF THE PARISH.

This cartoon, 'Death's Dispensary', was published in 1866.

● **SOURCE G**

It is now certain that the faulty water supply of a town is the main cause of the most terrible outbreaks of cholera, typhoid fever, dysentery and other similar illnesses. Dr Snow was not able to give proofs of his theory, but afterwards (and happily before his death in 1858) experiments established as almost certain that his guess had been right.

From the annual report by John Simon, Chief Medical Officer of Health, to the Privy Council in 1870.

● **SOURCE H**

The question as to whether the germs found in the bodies of those who died from cholera are definitely those of the cholera germ can now be considered closed. Cholera did not come into being spontaneously – out of nothing. It is a disease that attacks only those who have swallowed the comma-shaped germ.

From a report made by Robert Koch to the German government in 1884.

Questions

1 Study **Sources A** and **B**.
   Were these two sources produced for the same reason?
   Use the details of the sources and your knowledge to explain
   your answer.   [6]

2 Study **Source C**.
   'John Snow knew why so many people living in Soho caught cholera.'
   Do you agree with this statement?
   Use the source and your knowledge to explain your answer.   [6]

3 Study **Sources C** and **D**.
   Which of these sources is the more useful to a historian studying the
   cholera outbreak in 1854?
   Use the sources and your knowledge to explain your answer.   [7]

4 Study **Source E**.
   Why did most people at the time agree with the ideas in Source E
   rather than with Snow's ideas?
   Use the source and your knowledge to explain your answer.   [7]

5 Study **Source F**.
   Are you surprised that this cartoon was published in 1866?
   Use the source and your knowledge to explain your answer.   [7]

6 Study **Sources G** and **H**.
   Does Source G prove that the work of Koch was not important?
   Use the sources and your knowledge to explain your answer.   [7]

7 Study **all** the sources.
   'The work of John Snow was the most important development in the
   fight against cholera.' How far do the sources support this view?
   Use the sources and your knowledge to explain your answer.   [10]

SOURCE INVESTIGATION 10

Why did some people oppose public health reforms?

Read all the sources, then answer the questions on page 53.

As the nineteenth century progressed, demand grew for public health reforms such as the provision of clean drinking water and proper sewers. Progress was slow because of opposition to reforms. Was this opposition due to self-interest, such as people not wanting to pay for the improvements? Was it due to ignorance of what caused disease? Or were there other reasons?

● **SOURCE A**

A cartoon published in 1829. The caption is: 'MONSTER SOUP commonly called THAMES WATER, being a correct representation of that precious stuff doled out to us!'

● **SOURCE B**

A drawing published in 1832. The clothes of a patient who has just died of cholera are being washed in a stream from which people get their drinking water.

● **SOURCE C**

NOTICE!!!

We are credibly informed by a correspondent that the much-admired

JAPANESE CHEROOTS

are highly recommended by the faculty abroad as being a sure preventive of that raging disorder the

Cholera Morbus;

they have been recently imported into this Country, and are found to be of that mild and fragrant nature that they may be used by

The Fair Sex

without producing nausea. Their confirmed anti-contagious virtues and delicate fragrance have already procured them a very high and just estimation.

Vide Morning Herald, Nov. 12, 1831.

ARLISS, Printer, Addle Street, Wood Street, Cheapside

A cigar advertisement published in 1831.

● **SOURCE D**

A cartoon published in 1831. It shows where the Southwark Water Company in London got its water from.

● **SOURCE E**

	Number of houses	Deaths from cholera	Deaths in every 10,000 houses
Southwark Water Company	40,046	1,263	315
Lambeth Water Company	26,107	98	37
The rest of London	256,423	1,422	55

John Snow's calculations of the number of deaths in houses supplied by different water companies. The figures are for a seven-week period during the cholera outbreak in 1854.

● **SOURCE F**

A cartoon about the River Thames called 'The Silent Highwayman. Your money or your life', published in 1858.

● **SOURCE G**

The various forms of disease amongst the labouring classes are caused by atmospheric impurities [bad air] produced by decomposing animals and vegetables, by damp and filth, and close overcrowded buildings. The expense of refuse removal, public drainage and supplies of water would be a gain by reducing the existing cost resulting from sickness and death.

From Chadwick's *Report on the Sanitary Condition of the Labouring Population of Great Britain*, published in 1842.

● **SOURCE H**

The chief theme of the speakers in opposition to the sewage plan was related to saving the money of the ratepayers. An alternative plan was agreed that meant the main sewers would discharge their waters into the river at several points thereby continuing the pollution.

From a report about the conditions in Leeds in the early 1840s, written in 1844.

● **SOURCE I**

There is nothing a man hates so much as being cleaned against his will, or having his floors swept, his wall whitewashed, his pet dungheaps cleared away. It is a fact that many have died of a good washing. We prefer to take our chance with cholera than to be bullied into action. The truth is, Mr Chadwick has very great powers, but it is not easy to see what they can be used for.

From *The Times* newspaper, August 1854.

Questions

1 Study **Sources A** and **B**.
Does Source A make what the people are doing in Source B surprising?
Use the sources and your knowledge to explain your answer.   [8]

2 Study **Source C**.
Why were these cigars so popular at this time?
Use the source and your knowledge to explain your answer.   [7]

3 Study **Sources D** and **E**.
Does Source D show that John Snow's investigations were not important?
Use the sources and your knowledge to explain your answer.   [8]

4 Study **Sources F**, **G** and **H**.
Would the cartoonist (Source F) have agreed with Source G or Source H?
Use the sources and your knowledge to explain your answer.   [8]

5 Study **Source I**.
Is Source I a joke, or is the author serious?
Use the source and your knowledge to explain your answer.   [7]

6 Study **all** the sources.
'There was opposition to public health reforms because people did not understand that filthy conditions and dirty water helped spread disease.' How far do the sources support this statement?
Use the sources and your knowledge to explain your answer.   [12]

SOURCE INVESTIGATION 11

Who was the real 'Angel of the Crimea'?

Read all the sources, then answer the questions on page 56.

In 1854 Britain went to war with Russia and invaded the Crimea in southern Russia. News soon came back to Britain of the terrible conditions in the British military hospitals and the suffering of the wounded soldiers. There was a public outcry and in November 1854 the government sent Florence Nightingale and a group of nurses to the military hospital at Scutari in the Crimea.

Nightingale was soon bombarding the government with details of how terrible conditions were and with demands for supplies.

Shortly afterwards, another nurse arrived in the Crimea – Mary Seacole. She was born in Jamaica and had enormous experience as a nurse. When the British government ignored her offers of help she went to the Crimea at her own expense. She set up her 'British Hotel' where she supplied the soldiers with clean food and drink and dealt with a range of wounds and diseases.

Historians have been divided over which of these two women made the greatest contribution to the care of the wounded soldiers in the Crimea – who was the real 'Angel of the Crimea'?

● **SOURCE A**

On my very first day, a party of sick and wounded had just arrived. Here was work for me, I felt sure. So strong was the old impulse within me, that I did not wait for permission, but seeing a poor soldier stretched upon a pallet, groaning heavily, I ran up to him at once, and eased the stiff dressings. He had been hit in the forehead, and I think his sight was gone. I stooped down, and raised some tea to his baked lips. Then his hand touched mine and rested there.

From Mary Seacole's autobiography, published in 1857. It was called *Wonderful Adventures of Mrs Seacole in Many Lands.*

● **SOURCE C**

I have much satisfaction in being able to inform you that the hospital in Scutari is now in a highly satisfactory state and that nothing is lacking.

From a letter by Dr John Hall, Chief of Medical Staff of the army in the Crimea, to his superior in London, October 1854. He is describing conditions before Florence Nightingale arrived. Hall believed in strict discipline and did not want the troops to be 'pampered'.

● **SOURCE B**

It appears that in these hospitals no washing has been performed for the men of their bedlinen – except by ourselves. When we came here, there was neither basin, towel, nor soap in the Wards. The consequences of this are Fever, Cholera, Gangrene, Lice, Bugs, Fleas.

I always expected to end my days as Hospital Matron, but I never expected to be a kind of General Dealer in socks, shirts, knives and forks, wooden spoons, tin baths, tables, cabbages and carrots, operating tables, towels and soap. You can have little idea of the horror and misery of operating upon these dying and exhausted men. We now have four miles of beds. As I went on my night-rounds among the newly wounded that first night, there was not one murmur. These poor fellows bear pain with heroism.

Extracts from letters Florence Nightingale wrote to the British government soon after she arrived in the Crimea in November 1854.

● **SOURCE D**

Nightingale thought that male orderlies, not nurses, should be tending the sick. The nurses were there to give 'womanly attentions' like placing cologne-filled handkerchiefs next to the men's stinking stumps left after their limbs had been amputated.

Nightingale did not think it proper for female nurses to come into close contact with male nurses. She did not allow her nurses in the wards after 8.30 p.m., and she thought it was only acceptable for certain parts of men's bodies to be washed by the nurses. Bromide was given to the patients to curb their sexual urges. One of her nurses, Elizabeth Davies, wanted a more practical role. The only way of doing this was to leave Scutari against Nightingale's wishes and go nearer to the front.

From *The Crimean War* by Paul Kerr, published in 1997.

● **SOURCE E**

When Nightingale and her nurses arrived at Scutari, nearly two thousand wounded and sick lay in rat-infested wards. She immediately ordered three hundred scrubbing brushes. She organised the nursing of the sick. She provided meals, supplied bedding, and saw to the laundry. Her nurses bandaged the men's wounds while she sometimes held the hands of the dying. Within six months she had slashed the death rate.

A recent description of Florence Nightingale's actions.

● **SOURCE F**

A painting from 1855 of Florence Nightingale in Scutari Hospital. In 1855 a London newspaper began to call her 'the lady with the lamp', because of the popular idea that she walked the wards at night making sure the soldiers were comfortable.

● **SOURCE G**

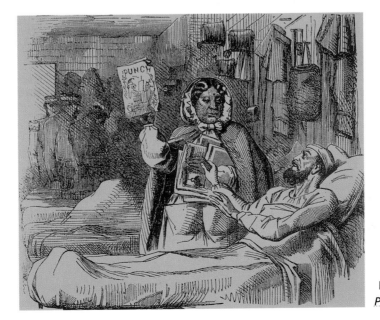

A drawing of Mary Seacole published in the British magazine *Punch*, May 1857.

● **SOURCE H**

Her hut was surrounded every morning by the rough navvies who had a faith in her skills in healing, which she justified by many cures and by removing cases of diarrhoea, dysentery, and similar complaints.

An eye-witness description of Mary Seacole written in 1855 by a journalist from *The Times.*

● **SOURCE I**

I will not call it a bad house – but something like it. Anyone who employs Mrs Seacole will introduce much kindness – but also much drunkenness and improper conduct.

From a letter by Florence Nightingale in 1870. She is writing to the man responsible for recruiting nurses for the Franco-Prussian War. Mary Seacole had applied for a job and asked Nightingale for a reference. At the top of the letter Nightingale had written 'Burn'.

● **SOURCE J**

It is now emerging that the 'Lady with the Lamp' was not really the best-loved nurse of the Crimean War. That honour belongs to Mary Seacole. It was she whom soldiers considered the true 'Mother of the Army'. While Miss Nightingale worked at the official hospital far from the fighting, Mrs Seacole set up her own supply store and medical unit just five miles from the fighting. While Miss Nightingale dismayed wounded officers by walking past their beds without even a word, Mrs Seacole went into the war zone armed with bandages and medicines, to look after the wounded.

From an article in *The Times*, 4 September 2000.

Questions

1 Study **Sources A** and **B**.
   How far did Florence Nightingale and Mary Seacole react in similar ways when they first got to the Crimea?
   Use the sources to explain your answer.   [7]

2 Study **Sources B** and **C**.
   Why do you think these two sources differ in their descriptions of conditions in the hospital at Scutari?
   Use the sources and your knowledge to explain your answer.   [8]

3 Study **Sources D** and **E**.
   Must one of these sources be wrong?
   Use the sources and your knowledge to explain your answer.   [7]

4 Study **Sources F** and **G**.
   Do you trust the impressions these two pictures are trying to make?
   Use the sources and your knowledge to explain your answer.   [8]

5 Study **Sources H** and **I**.
   Are you surprised by what Florence Nightingale has written in Source I?
   Use the sources and your knowledge to explain your answer.   [8]

6 Study **all** the sources.
   'Mary Seacole and not Florence Nightingale deserves to be called "The Angel of the Crimea".' How far do the sources convince you that this statement is right?
   Use the sources and your knowledge to explain your answer.   [12]

SOURCE INVESTIGATION 12

Did patients immediately benefit from Simpson's work on anaesthetics?

Read all the sources, then answer the questions on page 59.

A major problem in surgery was pain. This was because surgeons had no effective anaesthetics and patients often died from shock. This situation began to change in the nineteenth century. Humphrey Davy had already noticed that laughing gas relieved pain. In 1846 surgeons in America and Britain successfully used ether as an anaesthetic. Unfortunately, there were problems with ether – it irritated the lungs and made people sick. In 1847 James Simpson discovered that chloroform made a good anaesthetic. However, there was still a major problem to be faced: that of persuading people to accept the use of anaesthetics. Did Simpson's discovery really help people in the second half of the nineteenth century?

● **SOURCE A**

A drawing, published in 1793, of surgery taking place then.

● **SOURCE B**

We look back with sorrow on the methods of the opponents of Paré. In the course of years our successors will, I believe, look back with similar feelings on the so-called desirability of pain in operations as claimed by many surgeons at the present day. They will be amazed at the idea of men confessing that they prefer operating on their patients in a waking state instead of an anaesthetic state; and that the agonies which they inflict should be endured quietly. All pain is destructive and fatal.

From a speech Simpson gave to a medical meeting in 1847.

● SOURCE C

A teaspoonful of chloroform was inhaled from a handkerchief. In about half a minute, finding her unconscious, I requested Mr Lloyd to begin the operation. She gave a kick which made me think that the chloroform had not had sufficient effect. I was giving her more chloroform when her lips became suddenly blanched and she spluttered at the mouth. I threw down the handkerchief, dashed cold water in her face, and gave her some to drink, without any effect. The whole process of inhaling, operation and death could not have taken more than 2 minutes.

An account of the death of Hannah Greener, aged 15, in 1848, published in a medical journal. She was the first person to die under chloroform. Her operation was for the removal of a toenail.

● SOURCE D

It is repulsive to good taste that every woman about to go through childbirth, an ordeal to which she is doomed by the laws of Nature, should be made unconscious through the whole proceedings. (1848)

Pain has been invented by Almighty God. (1849)

The pain and sorrow of childbirth exert powerful and useful influence on the religious and moral character of women. (1853)

Extracts from letters to a medical journal.

● SOURCE E

Dr Snow gave me the blessed chloroform and the effect was mild, calming and beautiful beyond belief.

From Queen Victoria's journal, 1853, describing using chloroform during the birth of her eighth child.

● SOURCE F

Dr Hall takes this opportunity of warning medical officers against the use of chloroform in the severe shock of gunshot wounds, as he thinks few will survive if it is used. It is much better to hear a man scream lustily than to see him sink silently into his grave. But Dr Hall knows that public opinion, based on mistaken kindness, is against him.

From a notice issued by Dr John Hall in 1855 during the Crimean War. Hall was the Chief of Medical Staff of the British army in the Crimea.

● SOURCE G

A cartoon called 'Operation Madness'. It was published in 1870 when anaesthetics were beginning to be widely used.

DID PATIENTS IMMEDIATELY BENEFIT FROM SIMPSON'S WORK ON ANAESTHETICS? **59**

THE NINETEENTH CENTURY   THE NINETEENTH CENTURY   THE NINETEENTH CENTURY   THE NINETEENTH CENTURY   HE NINETEENTH CENTURY   THE NINE

● **SOURCE H**

A drawing of an operation around 1870.

Questions

1 Study **Source A**.
Does this source provide reliable evidence that eighteenth-century surgeons were clumsy and cruel?
Use the source and your knowledge to explain your answer. [6]

2 Study **Source B**.
Why do you think Simpson made this speech in 1847?
Use the source and your knowledge to explain your answer. [6]

3 Study **Sources C** and **D**.
How far does Source C support the arguments in Source D?
Use the sources and your knowledge to explain your answer. [7]

4 Study **Sources E** and **F**.
Are you surprised by Dr Hall's attitude towards chloroform?
Use the sources and your knowledge to explain your answer. [7]

5 Study **Source G**.
Why was this cartoon published in the 1870s?
Use the source and your knowledge to explain your answer. [7]

6 Study **Source H**.
How far does this source show that the use of chloroform solved the problems facing surgeons?
Use the source and your knowledge to explain your answer. [7]

7 Study **all** the sources.
How far do these sources show that the work of Simpson was of immediate benefit to patients?
Use the sources and your knowledge to explain your answer. [10]

SOURCE INVESTIGATION

13

How important was Pasteur's germ theory of disease?

> **Read all the sources, then answer the questions on page 63.**

Men, women and children have always suffered from illnesses, infections and various conditions that cause them pain and distress and that often shorten their lives. For hundreds of years societies have had different ideas about what caused disease and about which treatments were the most effective. Then, in 1861, Louis Pasteur published his 'germ theory' of disease – a completely new idea. Or was it?

● **SOURCE A**

A photograph of a bronze bleeding cup, used by the Ancient Greeks in the fifth century BC. It was heated and placed over a scratch made on the patient's back.

● **SOURCE B**

The Plague comes sometimes from the ground below, sometimes from the atmosphere above and sometimes from both together as we see a privy next to a bedroom, or anything else that corrupts the air. Sometimes it comes from the corruption of stagnant water in ditches.

The Plague sores are contagious because the humours of the body are infected and so the smell of such sores is poisonous and corrupts the air. In time of plague, people should not crowd together because some men might be infected. All four stinks are to be avoided – the stable, stinking fields or streets, dead carrion, and most of all stinking waters.

Therefore keep your house so that infected air cannot enter into it. Let your house be clean and make a clear fire of flaming wood. Fumigate it with herbs.

From *A Good Little Book against the Pestilence* by Bishop Aarhus, published in London in 1485.

● **SOURCE C**

Diseases such as scrofula can be cured if His Majesty touches the patient. It is not the air, nor the imagination, nor the token hung around the neck that brings the cure. It is the holy power of healing given to the King which is the cure.

From a book by Richard Wiseman, written in 1676. Richard Wiseman was a leading English surgeon and doctor to King Charles II.

● **SOURCE D**

A cartoon from 1849. It shows people a way of avoiding catching disease.

● **SOURCE E**

I place some liquid in a flask with a long neck. I boil it to kill the germs and let it cool. In a few days little animals will grow in it. If I repeat the experiment but draw the neck into a curve, but still open, the liquid will remain pure for three or four years. What difference is there between them? They both contain the same liquid and they both contain air. It is that in one, the dust in the air and its germs can fall in; in the other, they cannot. I have kept germs out of it and therefore I have kept Life from it. The doctrine of spontaneous generation is now dead.

Louis Pasteur describes the experiment he carried out in April 1864 to prove his germ theory.

● **SOURCE F**

Will you have some microbe? There is some everywhere. The worship of microbes is the fashion. It reigns undisputed. It is a idea which must not even be discussed, especially when the learned Monsieur Pasteur has pronounced the holy words 'I have spoken'. The microbe is, it is claimed, the only true explanation of disease and Pasteur is its prophet.

Part of an article about Pasteur's germ theory by Monsieur Rossignol, published on 31 January 1881.

● **SOURCE G**

DIPHTHERIA. SCROFULA. CHOLERA.

FATHER THAMES INTRODUCING HIS OFFSPRING TO THE FAIR CITY OF LONDON.
(A Design for a Fresco in the New Houses of Parliament.)

A cartoon published in 1858.

● **SOURCE H**

A photograph of people visiting the Christian shrine at Lourdes in France in the second half of the twentieth century. Thousands of Christians believe they will be cured there because it is a holy place where miracles happened in the past.

● **SOURCE I**

Monkshood

This remedy is to be used during the first stage of the measles when there is a sudden onset of fever, a skin rash, nasal discharge, reddened eyes, dry cough and restless sleep.

A herbal remedy for measles from a book abut homeopathy published in 1999.

● **SOURCE J**

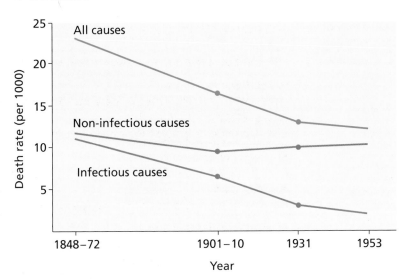

A graph showing the death rates from non-infectious and infectious diseases in England and Wales between 1848 and 1953.

● **SOURCE K**

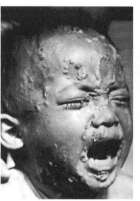

These photographs show an Indonesian boy who suffered from the disease yaws. They show him before and after he received an injection of penicillin.

Questions

1 Study **Sources A**, **B** and **C**.
Do these sources show similar or different ideas about disease?
Use the sources and your knowledge to explain your answer.   [6]

2 Study **Source B**.
We now know that Bishop Aarhus' ideas about what caused disease were wrong, However, thousands of copies of his book were sold. Why do you think this was?
Use the source and your knowledge to explain your answer.   [5]

3 Study **Sources A**, **B**, **C** and **D**.
Does Source D show that ideas about disease were changing or staying the same?
Use the sources and your knowledge to explain your answer.   [5]

4 Study **Sources E** and **F**.
How effective is Monsieur Rossignol (Source F) in destroying Pasteur's explanation in Source E?
Use the sources and your knowledge to explain your answer.   [6]

5 Study **Source G**.
Do you agree that the cartoonist must have known about Pasteur's germ theory?
Use the source and your knowledge to explain your answer.   [6]

6 Study **Sources H, I** and **J**.
How far does Source J make it difficult to understand why people are still using the cures in Sources H and I?
Use the sources and your knowledge to explain your answer.   [6]

7 Study **Source K**.
'These photographs show the results of penicillin, therefore they have nothing to do with Pasteur.' Do you agree with this statement?
Use the source and your knowledge to explain your answer.   [6]

8 Study **all** the sources.
'Louis Pasteur's germ theory was not important.' How far do the sources support this view?
Use the sources and your knowledge to explain your answer.   [10]

SOURCE INVESTIGATION 14

Penicillin: who can claim the credit?

Read all the sources, then answer the questions on page 67.

Penicillin came into use during the years 1942–45. To most people, it was a wonder drug that cured illnesses that earlier would have led to certain death. From this time until his death in 1955, Alexander Fleming got most of the credit for penicillin. He became a national hero in Britain and was honoured all over the world. In 1945, he was awarded the Nobel Prize for medicine. However, he had to share it with Ernst Chain and Howard Florey, who had helped develop the drug. Was this fair? Who should really get the credit?

● **SOURCE A**

A cartoon about Fleming's discovery of penicillin.

● **SOURCE B**

Fleming was in his little laboratory as usual, surrounded by dishes. He disliked being separated from his cultures before he was quite certain that there was no longer anything to be learned from them. He was often teased about his untidy habits. He was now to prove that untidiness may have its uses.

Fleming took up several old cultures and removed the lids. Several of the cultures had been contaminated with mould. 'As soon as you uncover a culture dish', he said to Pryce, 'something tiresome is sure to happen. Things fall out of the air.' Suddenly he stopped talking, then, after a moment's observation, said 'That's funny . . .'. On the culture at which he was looking, there was a growth of mould, as on several others, but on this particular one, all around the mould, the staphylococci germs had been dissolved.

Fleming took a little piece of the mould with his scalpel. He obviously wanted to make quite sure that this mysterious mould would be preserved. 'What struck me', Pryce says, 'was that he didn't confine himself to observing, but took action at once.'

From a biography of Fleming published in 1959.

● **SOURCE C**

There was a centuries old 'folk-medicine' tradition that various mouldy substances cured infections.

Details of one early use of penicillin came to light in 1940 when a former patient of Joseph Lister described the treatment she had received in 1884, when she was a young nurse. Injured in a street accident, she sustained a wound that became infected. Various antiseptics failed to clear the infection and then something was used that worked so dramatically that she asked that its name be written in her scrapbook. The word written in her book was Penicillium.

From a book about Fleming published in 1984.

● **SOURCE D**

Fleming used penicillin as a local antiseptic on a scientist's eye that had conjunctivitis. The infection cleared up, but when he used it in deep wounds it did not work. It also took a long time to produce enough penicillin to treat just one person.

In 1929 Fleming wrote all his findings in a paper. Nobody at the time took any notice. This was probably Fleming's fault. He had not tried injecting penicillin, he had only used it as a local antiseptic. This meant he had not provided the evidence that it was an important breakthrough. He did write at the time, 'It is quite likely that penicillin will be used in the treatment of septic wounds.'

A recent description of Fleming's early work with penicillin.

● **SOURCE E**

Penicillin has the promise of having practical uses in the treatment of infections. In view of the great practical importance of penicillin, it is proposed to prepare it in purified form suitable for injection and to study its antiseptic effects on living creatures.

Part of a letter written by Howard Florey on 6 September 1939 to the Medical Research Council in London.

● **SOURCE F**

The patient, a policeman, had had a sore on his mouth for about a month, and the infection had spread to his scalp. The infection had spread to both his eyes and one had been removed. He had an abscess on his lung – and was well on the way to death. We'd nothing to lose and everything to gain. So we thought we'd try penicillin.

The shortage of penicillin was such that after the first day I collected his urine and took it over to where Florey was working. The penicillin was extracted from the urine and used again.

On the fourth day, the patient was really dramatically improved. He was sitting up in bed and his temperature had gone down. On the fifth day, the penicillin began to run out and we couldn't go on. The patient gradually worsened and eventually died.

Professor C M Fletcher, a member of Florey's team, interviewed on TV in 1967, recalling the first human trial of penicillin in February 1941.

● **SOURCE G**

After discussing the matter with you last Friday, I have come to the conclusion that the only way in which your most important work on penicillin can be made to go forward is for you to go to the USA for three months. It is quite clear to me also that you cannot get penicillin produced by manufacturing firms in this country under present conditions.

From a letter from Florey's boss, Professor Mellanby, to Florey, April 1941. In the meeting on the Friday, Florey had suggested to Mellanby that he should go to the USA to produce penicillin.

● **SOURCE H**

This stained glass window shows Alexander Fleming working in his laboratory. It is in St James' Church, Paddington, close to St Mary's Hospital where Fleming worked for nearly all his career.

● **SOURCE I**

In your leading article on penicillin yesterday, you did not give anyone the credit for this discovery. I would, with your permission, like to point out that the credit should be given to Professor Alexander Fleming of this research laboratory, at St Mary's Hospital. He is the discoverer and the author of the original suggestion that penicillin might prove to have important uses in medicine.

From a letter from Sir Almoth Wright to *The Times* newspaper, 31 August 1942. Wright was Fleming's boss at St Mary's Hospital.

PENICILLIN: WHO CAN CLAIM THE CREDIT? **67**

THE TWENTIE
THE TWENTIETH CENTURY
THE TWENTIETH CENTURY
THE TWENTIETH CENTURY
THE TWENTIETH CENTURY
HE TWENTIETH CENTURY

● **SOURCE J**

My policy here has never been to interview the press nor allow them to get any information from us by telephone. I have kept to this in spite of protests from some of my colleagues, especially Ernst Chain.

In contrast, Fleming has been interviewed without cease, photographed, etc. (we have ample evidence of this here) with the result that he is put across as the discoverer of penicillin (which is true) with the implication that he did all the work leading to the discovery of its properties (which is not true).

Many of my colleagues feel things are going too far, and are getting unhappy at seeing so much of their own work going to glorify or even financially enrich someone else.

A letter from Howard Florey to the secretary of the Medical Research Council in London, written in January 1944.

Questions

1 Study **Sources A** and **B**.
'These two sources agree that Fleming's discovery of penicillin was a complete accident.' Do you agree?
Use the sources and your knowledge to explain your answer. [6]

2 Study **Source C**.
Does this source prove that Alexander Fleming did not discover penicillin?
Use the source and your knowledge to explain your answer. [6]

3 Study **Sources D**, **E**, and **F**.
How far do these sources show that it was Florey, not Fleming, who was important in the development of penicillin?
Use the sources and your own knowledge to explain your answer. [8]

4 Study **Source G**.
Are you surprised that Florey wanted to go to the USA in 1941?
Use the source and your knowledge to explain your answer. [7]

5 Study **Source H**.
'This stained glass window is of no use to a historian investigating the story of penicillin.' Do you agree?
Use the source and your knowledge to explain your answer. [6]

6 Study **Sources I** and **J**.
Was Florey right to be annoyed with Fleming?
Use the sources and your knowledge to explain your answer. [7]

7 Study **all** the sources.
'These sources show that Fleming deserved no credit for penicillin.'
How far would you agree with this statement?
Use the sources and your knowledge to explain your answer. [10]

SOURCE INVESTIGATION 15

Was the National Health Service welcomed?

Read all the sources, then answer the questions on page 70.

In 1942, the Beveridge Report was published. It was the work of a civil servant, Sir William Beveridge. In it he wrote that all citizens should have the right to be free from the five 'giants' of want, disease, ignorance, squalor and idleness. In 1945, the Labour Party came to power. Part of their plan of reconstruction after the Second World War (1939–45) was to set up a National Health Service. This was to be masterminded by Aneurin Bevan, the Minister of Health, and would attack one of Beveridge's 'giants', disease. In 1946, an Act of Parliament was passed and in 1948 the National Health Service was introduced into Great Britain. You would think everybody would have welcomed it – but did they?

● SOURCE A

For headaches, we had vinegar and brown paper. For whooping cough, we had goose fat rubbed on our chests. For mumps, we had stockings round our throats and for measles we had tea stewed in the teapot round the fire. All different kinds of home cures. My parents thought they were better than going to the doctor's and getting pills or medicine in a bottle. Well, they would, wouldn't they? They couldn't afford the doctor, who charged sixpence a visit.

From an interview with Kathleen Davies, who remembers life in Birmingham when she was a child in the 1930s.

● SOURCE B

Fathers and children at work come under the National Health Insurance. It is the mother who gets left out as far as treatment goes. She can go to hospital for teeth, but she cannot afford the transport or, as a rule, the time. She may get the family doctor for herself and the children if she pays into the medical club. If she does not pay in, she carries on as long as she can without advice or treatment. She will not start a doctor's bill for herself if she can possibly stand on her feet. My visits cost 6d each.

A district nurse explains how a family got health care in the 1930s.

● SOURCE C

A cartoon from the *Daily Mirror*, May 1946, commenting on Aneurin Bevan's appointment as Minister of Health. Harley Street was the street in London where fashionable doctors had their consulting rooms and charged their patients high prices.

HERE HE COMES, BOYS !

● **SOURCE D**

If a National Health Service is set up then doctors will no longer be independent. They will instead be technicians controlled by civil servants and by men and women entirely ignorant of medical matters. (1943)

If the Bill is passed, no patient or doctor will feel safe from interference by some government regulation. The Minister's spies will be everywhere. (1946)

These extracts are taken from the *British Medical Journal*, which is the official journal of the medical profession.

● **SOURCE E**

A cartoon published in 1948. The figure on the left is Aneurin Bevan. The words in the bowl say 'National Health Service'. The doctors on the right are saying 'It all tastes awful'.

● **SOURCE F**

A cartoon published in 1949. The nurse is shouting to the people in the queue, 'Dentist says if there are any more of you thinking of fitting one another up with National Health teeth for Christmas presents, you've had it.'

● **SOURCE G**

It is certain that some of the earnings of the working class are deliberately thrown away. The bookmaker probably takes as much of the working man's money as the pub. The word poverty cannot be properly applied to persons who might live in comfort if they did not waste money on betting and drink.

From *The Times* newspaper, December 1901.

● **SOURCE H**

Medical treatment should be made available to rich and poor alike according to medical need only. Worry about money in a time of sickness is a serious hindrance to recovery, apart from its cruelty. The records show that it is the mother in the average family who suffers most from the absence of a full health service. In trying to balance her budget she puts her own needs last. No society can call itself civilised if a sick person is denied medical help because of lack of money. The essence of a satisfactory health service is that the rich and poor are treated alike.

From a speech by Aneurin Bevan, Minister of Health, in 1946. He was trying to persuade people to support the National Health Service.

● **SOURCE I**

We are unable to accept the proposal to set up a national medical service based upon the family doctor. The habit of getting something for nothing will be encouraged which is bound to have a harmful effect on the morale of the people.

From a report by a group of doctors in 1946.

● **SOURCE J**

Outside the shops the longest queues of the war lined up to buy the Beveridge Report. Within two weeks of its publication a Gallup poll discovered that nineteen people out of twenty had heard of the report, and nine out of ten believed that its proposals should be adopted.

From a book published in 1971. It describes what happened when the Beveridge Report was published in 1942.

Questions

1 Study **Sources A** and **B**.
What can you learn from these two sources about health care in the 1930s?
Use the sources to explain your answer. [7]

2 Study **Sources C** and **D**.
Would the person who drew the cartoon (Source C) have agreed with the arguments being put forward in Source D?
Use the sources and your knowledge to explain your answer. [8]

3 Study **Sources E** and **F**.
'Both of these cartoons support the setting up of the National Health Service'. Do you agree?
Use the sources and your knowledge to explain your answer. [8]

4 Study **Sources G** and **H**.
Does Source G prove that Bevan (in Source H) was wrong?
Use the sources and your knowledge to explain your answer. [8]

5 Study **Sources I** and **J**.
Does Source J make you surprised by what the doctors said in Source I?
Use the sources and your knowledge to explain your answer. [7]

6 Study **all** the sources.
How far do these sources show that the National Health Service was welcomed?
Use the sources and your knowledge to explain your answer. [12]

Women in medicine: have attitudes changed?

Read all the sources, then answer the questions on page 73.

● **SOURCE A**

A certain girl, Hagnodice, as a young woman desired to learn the science of medicine. Because of this desire, she cut her hair, put on male clothing, and entrusted herself to a doctor for training. After learning this science, when she heard that a woman was having labour pains, she would go to her. And when the woman refused to entrust herself to Hagnodice, thinking she was a man, Hagnodice lifted her undergarment and revealed that she was a woman. She cured women marvellously.

From the writings of a Greek writer describing events in Ancient Greece in the third century BC.

● **SOURCE B**

Worthless and bossy women are overturning this profession. Possessing neither natural ability nor professional knowledge, they make the greatest possible mistakes, thanks to their stupidity, and very often kill the patients. For they work without wisdom and from no certain foundation of knowledge.

A complaint made by John of Mirfield, a physician at St Bartholmew's Hospital, London, in the fourteenth century.

● **SOURCE C**

Madame, I have this night taken your medicine, for which I heartily thank you, for it hath done me much good and hath caused the stone to break. But your medicine hath made me piss my bed this night, for which my wife hath sore beaten me.

Lord Edmund Howe writing to Lady Lisle in 1535 after taking a powder she prepared for him for a bladder stone.

● **SOURCE D**

To cure a burning fever, take diascordium one ounce; mithridate two ounces; syrup of lemons one ounce. Mix these with cardus benedictus water or angelica water quarter of a pint. Take three pints of small ale; three handfuls of sorrel; two handfuls of the tops of marigolds. Steep them in the ale all night and in the morning strain it hard and make a drink of it.

An extract from Lady Grace Mildmay's papers. She was born into a wealthy family in 1552, and when she grew up was expected to give medical care to the people on her family's estates. She read widely and knew about the work of Galen.

72 *PART 2 SOURCE INVESTIGATIONS*

● **SOURCE E**

A woodcut of women delivering a baby in the 1500s.
The men are studying the position of the planets.

● **SOURCE F**

Isabel Warwick has the skill in the science of surgery and has done good work. It is therefore agreed that she, upon her good behaviour, shall use her skills without being obstructed by any of the surgeons in the city.

Records of the city of York, 1572.

● **SOURCE G**

My maid being sick I paid for opening her vein 4d to the widow Rugglesford.
For looking after her I gave one shilling.
To old Bess, for tending her for three days and two nights I gave one shilling.
In all, two shillings and 4d.

From the diary of the Rev Giles Moore, 1667.

● **SOURCE H**

LADY-PHYSICIANS.

Who is this Interesting Invalid? It is young Reginald de Braces, who has succeeded in Catching a Bad Cold, in order that he might Send for that rising Practitioner, Dr. Arabella Bolus!

A cartoon published in the magazine *Punch* in 1865.

● **SOURCE I**

We consider that the mixture of sexes in the same class is likely to lead to results of an unpleasant character.

Lecturers are likely to feel inhibited because of the presence of females and will be unable to give a clear description of some necessary facts.

The presence of young females as spectators in the operating theatre is an outrage on our natural instincts and feelings. Their presence will destroy those sentiments of respect and admiration with which the female sex is regarded by all right-thinking men.

A statement made in 1861 by students at the Middlesex Hospital in protest against Elizabeth Garrett studying there to become a doctor.

Questions

1 Study **Source A**.
What can you learn from this source about attitudes in ancient Greece towards women in medicine?
Use the source to explain your answer. [5]

2 Study **Sources B** and **C**.
Does Source C support the claims made in Source B?
Use the sources and your knowledge to explain your answer. [7]

3 Study **Sources C** and **D**.
Why do you think wealthy and intelligent women like these two spent their time making herbal remedies?
Use the sources and your knowledge to explain your answer. [6]

4 Study **Source E**.
Would people of the time have thought that the men in this picture were wasting their time while the women were doing the important work?
Use the source and your knowledge to explain your answer. [7]

5 Study **Sources F** and **G**.
How far do these two sources show that women had been accepted as doctors?
Use the sources and your knowledge to explain your answer. [8]

6 Study **Sources H** and **I**.
How far do these two sources agree?
Use the sources and your knowledge to explain your answer. [7]

7 Study **all** the sources.
'Attitudes towards women in medicine have not changed over the years.' How far do the sources support this statement?
Use the sources and your knowledge to explain your answer. [10]

Hospitals through pictures

Study all the
pictures of hospitals
between 1400 and
today, then answer
the questions on
page 77.

● SOURCE A

A scene in a medieval hospital around 1400. The doctor is examining the patient's
urine while other people are praying. The lighted candle is to help the dying
man's soul get to heaven.

● **SOURCE B**

The Hôtel-Dieu in Paris, about 1500. You can see corpses being sewn into shrouds in full view of the patients.

● **SOURCE C**

Nuns at work in a ward in the Hôtel-Dieu in Paris in 1650.

● **SOURCE D**

A contemporary drawing of a hospital in 1566. In the centre, John Porter, a master surgeon, is arriving at the hospital.

● **SOURCE E**

A patient being visited at home by a doctor in the seventeenth century.

● **SOURCE F**

THEN.   NOW.

Published in a magazine for nurses in 1888.

● **SOURCE G**

A drawing of a women's ward in a London hospital in 1808.

● **SOURCE H**

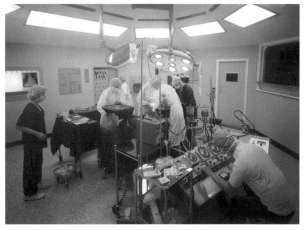

A photograph of a modern hospital.

Questions

1 Study **Source A**.
What does this source tell you about the treatment in medieval hospitals?
Use the source and your knowledge to explain your answer.   [7]

2 Study **Source B**.
What can you learn from this source about conditions in hospitals around 1500?
Use the source to explain your answer.   [6]

3 Study **Sources B** and **C**.
These two pictures show the same hospital at different times. How similar are they?
Use the sources to explain your answer.   [7]

4 Study **Sources A** and **D**.
How far does Source D show that conditions and treatments in hospitals had improved since the Middle Ages?
Use the sources to explain your answer.   [7]

5 Study **Source E**.
Why do you think this patient has decided to be treated at home and not in hospital?
Use the source and your knowledge to explain your answer.   [6]

6 Study **Source F**.
Why do you think this was published in 1888?
Use the source and your knowledge to explain your answer.   [7]

7 Study **Sources G** and **H**.
Why did hospitals develop more in the two hundred years after 1800 than in the thousands of years before?
Use the sources and your knowledge to explain your answer.   [10]

Revision charts

Chronology

Chronology means getting events in the right order. You need to know, for example, that the Romans came after the Greeks and were a long time before people like Pasteur and Lister in the nineteenth century. This timeline will help you get all this sorted out. Don't worry too much about exact dates, but do worry about getting the main periods in the right order and knowing roughly how far apart different periods were from each other, for example, which is the bigger gap – between prehistoric times and the Renaissance, or between the Renaissance and today?

Important people

Ibn al-Nafis shows that Galen was wrong – blood does not pass through the septum in the heart

Hippocrates: disease has natural causes and cures

Rhazes keeps alive Greek writings on medicine

Galen investigates how the body works and introduces the use of opposites

Prehistory – tens of thousands of years ago up to about 3000BC	Ancient Egypt 3000BC to about 300BC when the Greeks conquer the Egyptians	Ancient Greece 1000BC to about 250BC when the Romans take over the Greek Empire	Roman Empire about 200BC to about AD476	Middle Ages AD476–1450

Fall of Roman Empire

The Black Death

Christianity made official religion of Roman Empire

Islam founded – takes the lead in medicine until the Renaissance

Important events

When we are studying the history of medicine we divide up the past into the periods shown below. The most important individuals in the history of medicine have been added so you can see the whole picture. You need to be able to match each important individual with the right period. You also need to be able to say what they did.

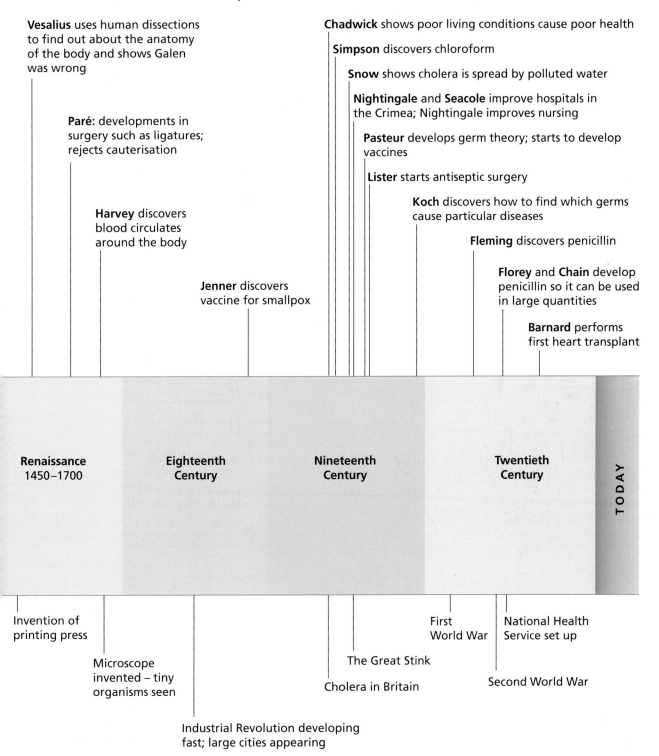

Ideas and treatments

People in the past have had many different ideas about what causes disease. These ideas can all be divided into two types – supernatural and natural. These are shown below the chart: those in red are supernatural and those in blue are natural. These different ideas have led to different treatments being used. Can you see the connection between ideas and treatments and can you work out which treatments are supernatural and which are natural?

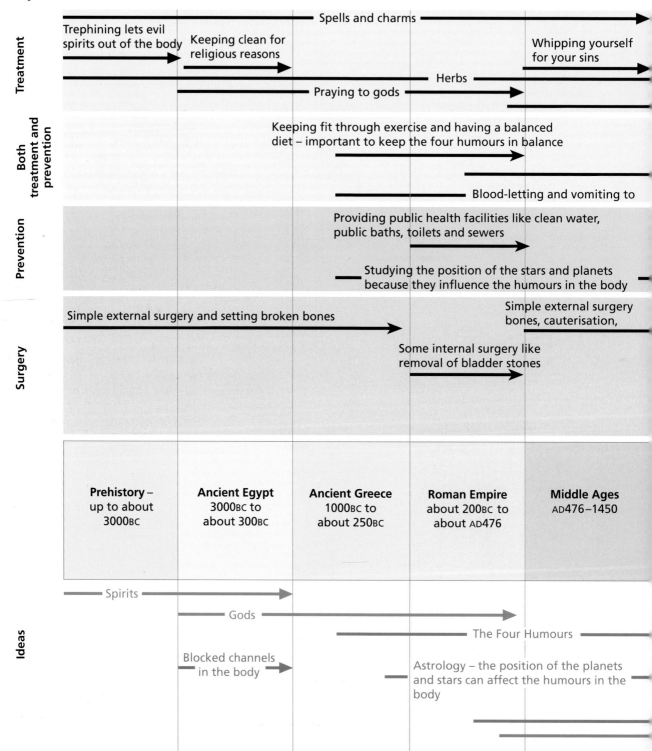

There are two important things for you to remember: **(i)** some ideas and treatments continued for a very long time; **(ii)** at nearly all times in the past supernatural ideas and treatments have existed alongside natural ones. Sometimes supernatural ideas were more important, at other times natural ideas were more important.

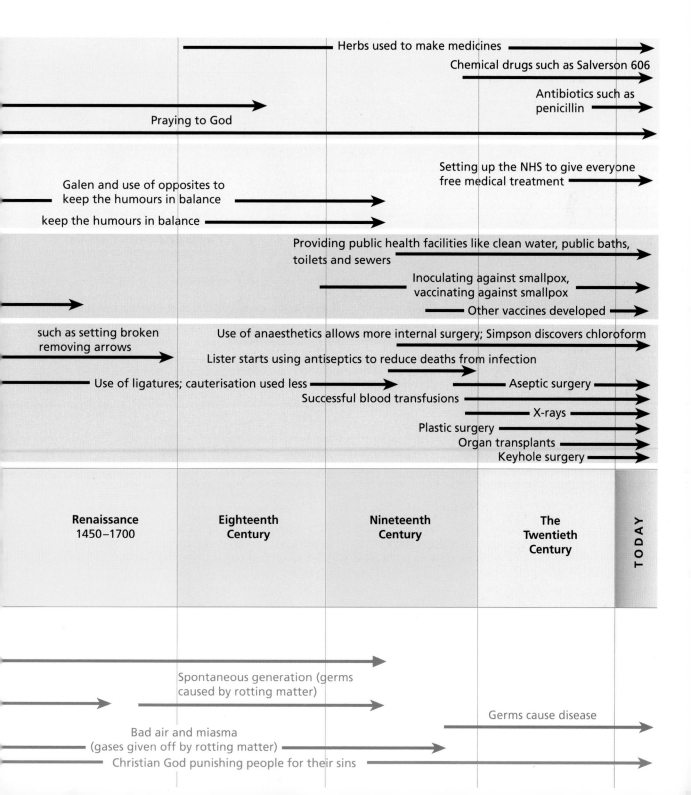

Herbs used to make medicines

Chemical drugs such as Salverson 606

Antibiotics such as penicillin

Praying to God

Setting up the NHS to give everyone free medical treatment

Galen and use of opposites to keep the humours in balance

keep the humours in balance

Providing public health facilities like clean water, public baths, toilets and sewers

Inoculating against smallpox, vaccinating against smallpox

Other vaccines developed

such as setting broken removing arrows

Use of anaesthetics allows more internal surgery; Simpson discovers chloroform

Lister starts using antiseptics to reduce deaths from infection

Use of ligatures; cauterisation used less

Aseptic surgery

Successful blood transfusions

X-rays

Plastic surgery

Organ transplants

Keyhole surgery

| Renaissance 1450–1700 | Eighteenth Century | Nineteenth Century | The Twentieth Century | TODAY |

Spontaneous generation (germs caused by rotting matter)

Germs cause disease

Bad air and miasma (gases given off by rotting matter)

Christian God punishing people for their sins

Factors

Improvements in medicine have sometimes been helped, or held up, by factors such as war or chance. There are often questions in the examination about these factors. Here are some lists of examples to help you prepare for such questions. Remember – these factors sometimes work together with other factors; as you can see from this illustration of Paré's discovery of an alternative to cauterising gunshot wounds. Try to find other examples.

Paré was working as a doctor in a war. The large number of wounded soldiers led him to run out of boiling oil. He had to find another method quickly.

Paré was working at the time of the Renaissance when people were ready to consider new ideas and methods. They did not assume the old methods were always the best.

This ointment is much better than boiling oil!

Paré himself is an important factor. He was clever enough to find a new method, brave enough to give it a go, and sensible enough to compare its results with those of the old method of boiling oil.

The fact that Paré ran out of oil and had to find a new method was chance. What if he had had enough oil?

Use specific examples, don't waffle

Do not give general answers such as 'War helped because it gave doctors more practice in treating wounds'. Use a specific example such as how war helped Paré. When you go into the exam room make sure you know two or three examples of each factor helping or hindering. When you write your answer make sure you use these examples. The questions often ask whether a factor like war helped or hindered medicine, so you need to explain examples of both.

Don't just describe an example of a factor

For example, you must not simply tell the story of Paré running out of boiling oil – you must explain **how** this helped him discover a new method. Once you have explained examples of war both helping and hindering, you need to reach your conclusion – did war help more than it hindered? There is no right answer to this question. The examiner is interested in what you think, as long as you can back it up with examples and explanation.

What a surprise!

Chance (or just being lucky?)

This is a difficult one for two reasons. First, it is difficult to decide if something was chance or not. Students often use Jenner's knowledge that dairymaids never caught smallpox and Simpson's discovery of chloroform as examples of chance. These are doubtful because everybody knew about dairymaids and cowpox, while Simpson was deliberately testing a ranges of substances when he discovered chloroform. There are many examples of people's lifestyles having an impact on medicine, for example, the creation of large industrial cities leading to problems of public health. Is this chance? Second, chance can never cause developments by itself – it still needs someone to recognise the importance of what has happened and to develop and use it. Remember that Pasteur said 'chance only favours prepared minds'.

Listed below are examples of real chance events helping medicine. There are not many.

1 Paré has some luck

In 1536, when he was treating gunshot wounds, Paré ran out of boiling oil and this made him use a soothing ointment instead. This worked much better and so people gradually stopped using boiling oil.

2 Pasteur's lazy assistant

In 1879 Pasteur's assistant was meant to have injected chickens with the chicken cholera germ. He was in such a rush to get off on his holidays that he forgot. The germs were left on a shelf where they were weakened by exposure to the air. When he came back he injected the chickens. Pasteur was amazed when they did not die. They still did not die when given another injection of fresh germs. Pasteur realised that the weakened germs had stimulated the body to fight future attacks of the germ. He then knew how vaccination works!

3 Fleming's messy laboratory

Scientists must like going on holiday – here is another example! In 1928 Fleming went on holiday leaving a dreadful mess of culture plates on his desk. When he got back and was tidying them up he noticed a large blob of mould had grown on one of the plates. Around this blob all the staphylococcal germs had been killed! Penicillin had been discovered.

If you answer a question about chance **use these three examples**. They are easily the best, and they are simple to explain.

Lifestyle

There are many examples of the way people lived either helping medicine or making things much worse.

1 Prehistoric people helped themselves keep healthy by being nomads. Because they did not live in the same place all the time they did not pollute their water supply or build up great piles of filth near where they lived. The fact that they were not farmers meant they did not catch diseases from cattle.

2 When prehistoric people began to be farmers they caught more diseases because **(i)** they lived in groups with other people and diseases spread between them, and **(ii)** diseases spread from their animals because the animals polluted the water and carried disease-bearing fleas.

3 The Egyptians had to build irrigation channels from the River Nile to the nearby land so they could grow crops. If the channels were blocked the land returned to desert and the crops died. This gave the Egyptians the idea for the first natural explanation of disease – that human illness was caused by channels in the body being blocked.

The channels are blocked!

4 When great industrial towns and cities appeared in the eighteenth and nineteenth centuries, public health became a real problem. The conditions in these towns were awful and they led to public health reforms in the nineteenth century.

Religion

You might think that a belief in supernatural causes and cures can only hold back progress in medicine. If you think illness is caused by supernatural forces, why bother trying to develop cures? However, belief in spirits and gods has often led to important advances being made in medicine, although it has also held up progress.

There are lots of examples for religion. **Use the ones you know most about** and remember that religion both helped and held up progress in medicine.

1 When the Egyptians took out organs from the body for preserving for the next life they learnt a lot about the body. But religious beliefs also stopped them dissecting the body, so they couldn't learn any more.

But …

2 The Egyptians also believed that keeping clean was a way of being at peace with the gods so they went to a lot of trouble to keep themselves clean.

3 Greeks went to Ascelpions to pray to the god Asclepius to heal them. However, while they were there they were able to rest, take exercise and follow a good diet. So although they went there for religious reasons, they were often cured by natural methods!

What would God want me to do?

4 The Christian religion dominated Europe in the Middle Ages. It taught that diseases were a punishment from God for people's sins, so there was no point in trying to find cures. All you could do was pray.

But …

5 Christianity taught that Christians should show compassion for their fellow humans by caring for the sick. The Church set up hosptials, and monasteries cared for the sick and preserved Greek medical writings.

Also …

6 Remember Galen and how his ideas dominated medicine in the Middle Ages? This was because the Christian Church liked his ideas because he believed that the human body had been created by one god and was ruled over by the soul. This fitted in well with Christian, and later, Muslim beliefs so both religions supported his ideas.

But …

7 Was this a good thing? Galen's ideas might have been a big step forward in his time and still helped doctors in the Middle Ages but when people like Vesalius and Harvey began to challenge Galen and to make further progress they were opposed because people claimed that going against Galen was going against God!

8 In the nineteenth century some people opposed Jenner's vaccination for smallpox because they said it was against God's will to transfer an animal disease to humans. They also claimed that smallpox was a punishment by God for leading an immoral life. The only answer was to lead a good life – not vaccination.

9 Also in the nineteenth century, some people opposed the use of anaesthetics during surgery. They were particularly against its use for childbirth and claimed God had wanted this to be painful. According to them, surgeons like Simpson, who used chloroform, were going against God's will.

What about Islam?

10 Muslims collected, preserved and improved on Greek medical writings – this is how many Greek ideas were introduced back into Europe later in the Middle Ages.

11 Muslims believed that God cured people through doctors and so people were encouraged to go to doctors. Islam taught that the sick should be looked after and that people should keep themselves clean, so many hospitals were built and people were encouraged to wash regularly.

But …

12 Islam disapproved of dissection and Muslims learned little about anatomy.

Washing seems to keep me healthy!

exam tip

Get your gods right!

Students sometimes write very vague answers about religion and refer to gods in a very general way. Remember: prehistoric people believed in spirits and charms; the Egyptians, Greeks and Romans believed in many different gods; from the time of the Romans many people have believed in the Christian God and many others have believed in the Islamic God Allah.

Communications

1 The Egyptians developed a system of writing called hieroglyphics. This meant they could write down what they learned about medicine. They gradually built up an enormous amount of knowledge about the body and treatments, which was handed on to later generations.

2 In 1450 the printing press was invented. Books about new ideas (such as those by Vesalius) could now be printed in their thousands, spreading new ideas all over Europe. But remember that new ideas could only spread at the speed of a galloping horse!

3 In the late nineteenth and twentieth centuries it became much easier to spread new ideas because of telephones, radio, TV and e-mail. Today, word of a new development can be broadcast around the world in seconds. In the past it took decades. Railways and air travel make it easier for scientists and doctors to get together to share new ideas.

Science, technology and art

1 The Greeks observed the natural world very carefully. They decided that everything was made from four basic elements: water, earth, fire and air. This led them to the Theory of the Four Humours and a natural explanation of disease.

2 The Romans were superb engineers. This was why they were able to build their great aqueducts and their sewers and public baths.

3 In the Renaissance, artists like Leonardo da Vinci began to base their drawings on dissected bodies. They were interested in getting every detail right and knowledge of anatomy grew fast. Vesalius certainly benefited from such drawings.

4 Also, the Renaissance was a time when people were again observing the natural world carefully, finding out for themselves, testing ideas and making many new discoveries. Inventions like the mechanical water pump helped Harvey come up with the idea of the heart pumping blood. The method of testing everything led to Paré conducting his experiment on bezoar.

5 Pasteur is a good example to use of how the needs of industry have led to developments in medicine. On many occasions Pasteur was asked to help French industries: when their alcohol was going sour he discovered the micro-organisms that caused this; he helped the wine growers by finding the germs that made their wine go bad and by developing pasteurisation to kill the germs; and finally he helped the silkworm industry by showing how a disease in silkworms was spread by an organism in the air. All these were important developments in Pasteur's work on germs and each time the needs of French industry were the cause.

6 Lister got the idea of using carbolic acid to fight infection during operations from the sewage system in Carlisle. There sewage was treated with carbolic acid, which led to less smell and the destruction of parasites living on the sewage.

7 In the late nineteenth and twentieth centuries developments in chemistry and industry were very important. New and better materials were developed, leading to more powerful microscopes and the development of synthetic drugs like Salverson 606. Industry made possible the mass production of penicillin and new technology led to the development of heart–lung machines and even artificial hearts.

8 Developments in science led to the discovery of X-rays. We can now scan patients to find out where, for example, bullets or gallstones are in the body, or can study a bone fracture in detail. X-rays have led to much better diagnoses.

War

Millions of people have been killed in war but sometimes war has helped progress in medicine. There have also been times when it has held up progress.

1 The Roman Empire depended on the Roman Army for its survival. The soldiers had to be kept healthy so hospitals, bath houses, latrines and aqueducts were built.

But ...
2 When the Roman Empire fell there was great chaos in Europe for a long period and many of the advances made by the Greeks and Romans were lost. Greek medical knowledge and Roman public health systems were replaced by folk medicine and supernatural approaches.

3 When Paré was working as a doctor with the French army in the 1530s he ran out of oil used for cauterising wounds. In the middle of a war, with injured soldiers suffering from dreadful gunshot wounds, he had to use what was handy and made up a soothing ointment that worked much better.

4 In the second half of the nineteenth century Pasteur and Koch were great rivals because one was French and the other was German, and their two countries were also great rivals. They both wanted to make discoveries first for the glory of their own country. This drove both of them on to greater discoveries about germs and vaccines.

I've made a great discovery!

5 In 1900 it was discovered that 40 per cent of the men volunteering to join the British army to fight in the Boer War were too unhealthy and unfit to be soldiers! This was one of the things that persuaded the Liberal Government to start making health and welfare improvements in 1906.

6 Alexander Fleming worked as a doctor in the First World War. He saw that synthetic antiseptics were not working with deep wounds. The sufferings of the patients whom he could not help made him determined to find better treatments after the war – this started him on the path to the discovery of penicillin.

7 Another valuable development in the First World War was the early work on plastic surgery. The terrible wounds suffered by soldiers, caused by new weapons, made its development very important. Further developments were made in the Second World War, by people like McIndoe, and during the Vietnam War.

What luxury!

8 During the Second World War many poor children were evacuated from cities to live with families in the country. Many of these families were appalled when they realised how malnourished these children were and that many of them had never seen water come out of taps or flushing lavatories. This made many people determined to improve things once the war was over. There was a sense that after the war a better world would be created. This led to the setting up of the National Health Service in 1948 which gave everyone free health care.

9 In 1939, at the beginning of the Second World War, Florey and Chain applied to the British government for a grant to help them continue their work on penicillin. The government was more concerned about the war effort and could not see what penicillin had to do with the war. It gave them £25!

But ...
10 In 1942 the USA entered the Second World War. The American government could see that penicillin could be of great benefit to their soldiers so they funded several chemical companies to mass-produce penicillin in enormous vats. Without this, penicillin would not have been created in large enough quantities to be of any use.

Epidemics

An epidemic is a serious outbreak of disease when far more people than usual are dying. Sometimes such epidemics have led to improvements in medicine.

1 The Plague in the fourteenth and seventeenth centuries led to governments acting to try to stop it spreading.

What a stink!

2 In the nineteenth century, outbreaks of cholera (and the Great Stink of 1858) forced the British government to pass measures like the Public Health Acts of 1848 and 1875. These gave local councils power to improve public health and to levy taxes to pay for the improvements.

Governments

1 The Roman government supplied Rome and many other cities with clean water, sewers, public toilets and baths. All this helped keep people healthy.

2 When the Plague hit Europe in the fourteenth and seventeenth centuries, governments helped by introducing regulations about isolating the sick, cleaning streets and the burial of infected bodies. Some cities introduced quarantines.

But …
As soon as the plague was over many governments went back to doing nothing!

3 In the eighteenth and early nineteenth centuries, when problems of public health in the growing towns and cities were getting worse, British governments refused to do anything because they believed in 'laissez-faire'.

However …
4 In the second half of the nineteenth century they started to act and local councils were given the power to improve public health. This led to the Great Clean-up – slums were knocked down and clean water and flushing lavatories connected to sewers were provided for many houses.

5 The Liberal government that came to power in 1906 believed there were many poor people who were not able to help themselves. They needed the government to help them. Between 1906 and 1912 a whole range of reforms was introduced including school clinics, medical inspections, free school meals and old age pensions.

Dinner's on me!

6 In 1939, when Florey and Chain asked for a grant from the British government to help them develop penicillin it gave them only £25, but the American government paid some of their chemical firms to mass-produce penicillin so that there was enough to be used on wounded soldiers.

There have also been many examples of people opposed to the idea of the government getting involved in medicine, such as: (i) the opposition to nineteenth-century public health reforms because of ideas of laissez-faire; (ii) opposition to the government making the smallpox vaccination compulsory; and (iii) opposition to the National Health Service.

Other factors

There are many other factors that have helped, or held up, developments in medicine. Here are a few of them.

Vested interest

This means that someone either benefits financially from keeping things as they are or benefits from the changes.

The best examples of this are:

- Inoculators opposed Jenner's smallpox vaccine because it would put them out of business.
- Surgeons who had built their reputations on the speed with which they could complete operations opposed the use of anaesthetics because being able to operate quickly was no longer important.
- Fairly wealthy people in the nineteenth century opposed paying higher rates to pay for public health improvements. Why, they said, should they pay to keep other people clean? It was the job of everyone to keep themselves clean.

Teamwork

In recent times science and medicine have become so complicated that it has become very difficult for one person to make discoveries alone. Working in a team has become much more important.

Examples include Pasteur and the discovery of the chicken cholera vaccine; the discovery of Salverson 606; and the work of Florey and Chain.

Conservatism

People have often opposed new ideas just because they are new. People have felt secure with old ideas that they are used to and feel threatened by new ideas, because they don't think they are safe or will work. Examples include opposition to Vesalius and Harvey challenging Galen's ideas; opposition to smallpox vaccination; opposition to the use of anaesthetics and antiseptics; and opposition to Pasteur's germ theory.

The medicine game

The game overleaf tells the story of the history of medicine. It shows some of the important developments and some of the things that slowed down progress. But it is not complete – there are lots of factors missing!

You need to complete the game before you can play it. On the copy your teacher has given you, fill in the white squares with either developments that helped medicine progress or factors that held things up.

For all the blue and white squares draw a green arrow pointing forwards for factors that help; draw a red arrow pointing backwards for factors that hold things up (see squares 1, 3 and 5). You also need to decide how important each factor was and show this by writing different numbers of squares to move on the arrows.

Make sure the factors you add to the game are in the right chronological place.

When you have finished you can play the game with counters and dice.

Points for discussion

- Which were the five most important factors?
- Which supernatural, and which natural ideas about disease are on the game?
- Does the game distort the history of medicine in any way?

The rules for the medicine game can be found on page 89.

Index